HODDER GEOGRAPHY

Series Editor: JEFF BATTERSBY Series Consultant: ROBERT PROSSER

SUSTAINABILITY & THE ENVIRONMENT

Dick Palfrey
Angela Gray

Hodder & Stoughton

A MEMBER OF THE HODDER HEADLINE GROUP

Acknowledgements

The authors would like to thank the following for permission to reprint copyright photographs in this book: Figure 1.11, FARM AFRICA; Figure 2.1, Vauxhall, and Lowe Howard-Spink; Figure 2.17, Corbis; Figure 3.1, Figure 3.18, Figure 4.9, Life File; Figure 3.16, Hutchison; Figure 3.24, First Hydro; Figure 4.3, Panos; Figure 4.12, Skyscan.

All other photographs supplied by the authors and the publisher.

The publishers would like to thank Ordnance Survey for permission to reproduce copyright material.

Every effort has been made to contact the holders of copyright material used in this book, but if any has been overlooked, the publishers will be pleased to make the necessary alterations at the first opportunity.

Orders: please contact Bookpoint Ltd, 39 Milton Park, Abingdon, Oxon OX14 4TD.
Telephone: (44) 01235 400414, Fax: (44) 01235 400454. Lines are open from 9.00–6.00, Monday to Saturday, with a 24 hour message answering service. Email address: orders@bookpoint.co.uk

British Library Cataloguing in Publication Data
A catalogue record for this title is available from The British Library

ISBN 0 340 70199 4

First published 1998

Impression number	10	9	8	7	6	5	4	3	2	1
Year	2004	2003	2002	2001	2000	1999	1998			

Cover photo from Corbis.

Typeset by Wearset, Boldon, Tyne and Wear.
Printed in Hong Kong for Hodder & Stoughton Educational, a division of Hodder Headline Plc, 338 Euston Road, London NW1 3BH by Colorcraft Ltd.

CONTENTS

Chapter 1

A World of Ideas and Systems **Pages 1–14**

Chapter 2

What Mother Earth throws up!! **Pages 15–26**

Chapter 3

Energy – May the Force be with you! **Pages 27–48**

Chapter 4

Humans as balancers **Pages 49–60**

GLOSSARY

Agenda 21 International agreement signed in 1992 at the Earth Summit in Rio de Janeiro. It sets out an international 'Code of Conduct' for the 21st century to ensure a sustainable and healthy future for all.
absorbtion Part of the Water Treatment Process: water passes through Granular Activities Carbon, attracting impurities and the elements which can affect taste and odour.
carbon dioxide emissions The production of carbon dioxide as a by product of combustion – the burning of hydrocarbon fuels.
cash crop An agricultural product grown for money.
clarification Part of the Water Treatment Process – the coagulation and filtering off of solid matter.
climatic change Permanent modification of the average climate, e.g. global warming, desertification and ozone depletion.
core The very dense central part of the Earth which when compared to an apple is equivalent to the core.
crust The rigid part of the lithosphere. Solid rocks near the Earth's surface which when compared to an apple is thinner than the skin.
deforestation The removal of trees from large forested areas for a variety of purposes, timber, resettlement, mining, ranching, communications etc. Commonly associated with the tropical rainforest, but is also a process that is associated with other types of forest, e.g. Taiga in Russia.
energy portfolio The mix of energy sources used by a country to generate its power. This may be strongly influenced by the natural resources the country possesses.
epicentre Point on the Earth's surface immediately above the focus.
final ozonation Part of the Water Treatment Process – when the water receives a final treatment of ozone to break down any remaining substances impinging on the purification.
focus Point beneath the ground where earthquake tremors originate, e.g. where plates snag and then slip.
fossil fuels Hydrocarbons, e.g. coal, oil and gas, formed millions of years ago under geological conditions. Regarded as non renewable because they are used far faster than they can be replaced.
global warming The raising of the average world temperature through the processes of industrialisation and urbanisation.
human made asset Resources which have been engineered by people.
impacts The result of an action or process.
inputs Flows into a system. Can be financial, environmental, ecological, social or political.
mantle Deep seated semi molten or 'plastic' like rock under great temperature and pressure. It is found under the crust. When compared to an apple is equivalent to the thickness of the flesh.
natural assets Valuable natural resources that a country may possess and can be manipulated/processed to order.
non renewable resources An energy source which is consumed far faster than it can be formed, e.g. coal, oil, gas.
nuclear energy An energy source derived from the process of splitting atoms of radioactive fuel under controlled conditions.
outputs Products of a system or part of a system.
pre-ozonation Part of the Water Treatment Process – the first time ozone is added to kill harmful bacteria and pollutants.
processes The mechanism for the change of inputs once they are in a system. Can be a natural process or a human process.
renewable energy An energy source that if properly managed and manipulated can be reused, e.g. hydroelectric power (HEP). Or an energy source that can be regrown, e.g. timber. It is sustainable.
screening Part of the Water Treatment Process – when water passes through screens that remove any debris and filter the flow.
seismal lines Contours drawn on a map of the Earth's surface to join places of equal seismic strength together.
shockwaves Energy transferred through the crust from an earthquake.
subsystem A small working unit as part of a larger system.
sustainability The ability to be able to manage resources so that they can replace themselves.
system A functional unit made of a series of interlinked parts. A system contains inputs, processes and outputs.
Water Treatment Process The process used to ensure that water is available for drinking, e.g. it has been purified.

A WORLD OF IDEAS AND SYSTEMS

1

Key Idea

Have you ever wondered where we come from, what we are doing here, and where we are going? It is important to make a study of systems and how everything fits together. Human activities can affect natural systems and natural systems can be adapted by people. Human activities need careful management so that they do not harm natural systems. The aim of this chapter is to introduce you to some basic ideas that will be explored throughout the book.

The whole system

The whole system is Planet Earth. As suggested your brain may hurt thinking about it, but you are a part of this system you are a **sub system** within the whole part. One of many different parts that make up the world in which we live. Enjoy your voyage of discovery as you find out more about where everything fits together.

RESOURCE 1.1
The whole system.

RESOURCE 1.2
A Philosophical Beginning.

Planet Earth condensed 4,600 million years ago from hot gases and cosmic dust. It cooled into a beautiful blue orb, slightly squashed at one pole but still easy to fall in love with. Barring accidents, like the sun going out, it will be here for another 10,000 million years.

If the Earth were only a few feet in diameter, floating a few feet above a field somewhere, people would come from everywhere to marvel at it. People would walk around it marvelling at its big pools of water, its little pools and the water flowing between. People would marvel at the bumps on it and the holes in it. They would marvel at the very thin layer of gas surrounding it and the water suspended in the gas. The people would marvel at all the creatures walking around the surface of the ball and at the creatures in the water. The people would declare it as sacred because it was the only one, and they would protect it so that it would not be hurt. The ball would be the greatest wonder known, and people would come to pray to it, to be healed, to gain knowledge, to know beauty and to wonder how it could be. People would love it and defend it with their lives because they would somehow know that their lives could be nothing without it. If the Earth were only a few feet in diameter.

It may seem big to us but Earth is a tiny speck in a universe so huge that your brain hurts just thinking about it.

1. Using the information from **Resource 1.1** draw pictures to show the different parts of the Earth. Add suitable annotations to your images to describe and explain what your diagram shows.

   Congratulations! You have just completed your own world. Is it something people would come and admire?

What is a system?

Without systems we would not function. Your body is a system, the school you attend has systems, the products you use have all been processed through a system. The very best system of all is that of Nature. It is a finely tuned system where each part, no matter how small, has a significant part to play in the functioning of the whole. We are part of that system, but far too often we upset the balance that has been created. We need to understand systems so that we can survive and not destroy what gives us life. This book will help you to understand some of the issues associated with this topic.

YOUR BODY AS A SYSTEM

Resource 1.3 shows how the body works as a system. All sorts of systems need inputs and outputs in order to work. Within the larger systems there are sub-systems; the way the legs work is a sub-system of the whole body. However small and unimportant a part of the body might appear to be, it is, in fact, essential to the working of the body as a whole. If one of these sub-systems breaks down, the larger system is at threat. The body itself is a sub-system of the wider world as people make up part of the planet.

RESOURCE 1.3
Your body as a system.

2. The following words are associated with the functioning of systems: **Inputs Processes Outputs**. Write a definition of each of these words.
3. Using the framework below to help you, draw a diagram of the way a system is constructed, filling in the spaces with the words above.
4. Think of another system (perhaps a car or a forest). Draw a new diagram using the same basic framework in question to illustrate the inputs, outputs and processes of this system.

A system at work

Now we will take a closer look at a system at work using an example of a system that we all use daily. The journey water takes from falling as rain to coming through our tap is illustrated in **Resource 1.4**. If you can see how this system works you will be much better placed to understand the systems in the natural world, which are often considerably more complex, whilst still operating in basically the same way.

RESOURCE 1.4
The Water Treatment process.

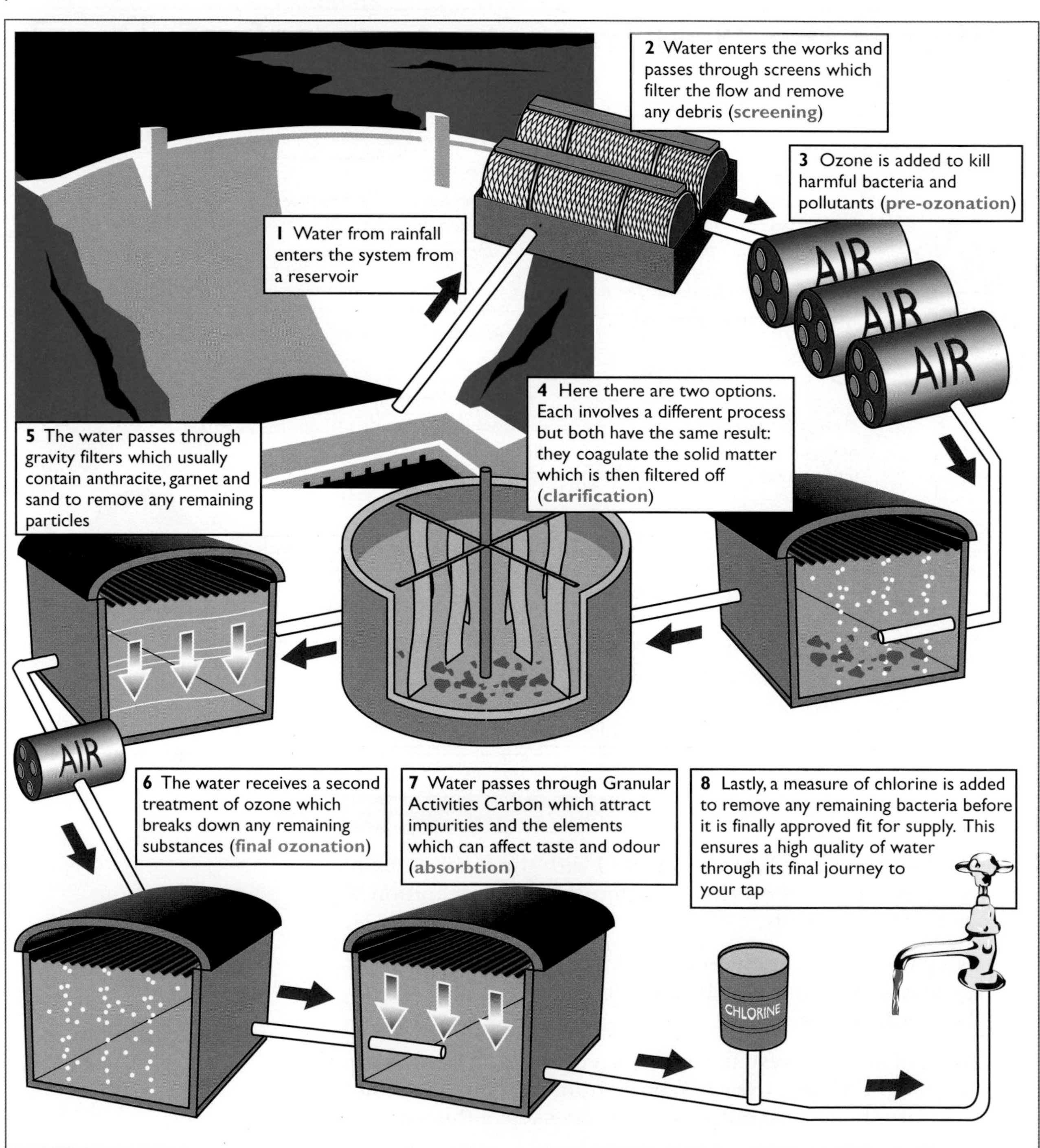

5. From **Resource 1.4** give an example of the following
   - a store of water
   - a flow of water (i.e. between where and where?)
   - an input of water to the system
   - an output from the system
   - a feedback
   - a process
   - a time-lag or delay in the system
6. Describe and explain what would happen to the system in
   - a severe and prolonged drought
   - times of excessive rainfall
7. Explain how, in normal periods, the system remains in perfect balance or equilibrium whilst still being a moving or dynamic system.
8. Give an example of the way systems are made up of smaller sub-systems which nest within the larger-scale system of which they form a part.

Systems can be natural or made by humans or the combination of both. The **Water Treatment Process** is an example of one that combines a natural system (rainfall) and a human system (the water treatment plant). Throughout this book you will study systems that have been adapted by human activity. You are now equipped to examine the ways humans have attempted to manage the natural world and why it is important to understand how systems work. And remember, whether it is entering a classroom, handing a book in or simply getting a drink of water – you have got to have a system.

Timescales and recovery rates

How many times have you thought this journey is really dragging? Sometimes it seems you have to wait forever for the next important event in your life such as your birthday or the next summer holidays. 'Time drags' is a common expression. And yet, our life time is very short compared to the length of time it can take for an oak tree to grow to maturity, a cliff to be eroded by the sea, or for a river to change its course.

RESOURCE 1.5
How long have we been here?

Look at **Resource 1.5** which shows how long Homo Sapiens (humans) have been around. The cartoon shows that if you imagine the whole history of the Earth from its formation as having taken place during one month (1 day = 150 million years), humans will have only been here for a minute. Sometimes we need to adjust our view of time in order to understand how the processes of the natural environment work and how long it can take something to grow, change or recover. In this section we look at different timescales and explore what we can measure by them.

Any activity in which you are involved has an impact. It has an effect on you, the people around you and the environment you have used. Involvement in any activity means that energy is exerted. After the event, time is needed to recover. For example, on Sports day after you have taken part in a race, you will need time to recover. The grass will also take time to recover as you will have trampled on it. The rate at which you and the grass recover will be different. You will take a few minutes, the grass will need longer.

It may be a natural event that has an impact on the environment such as an ice age, a flood or volcanic eruption. It could be an event that is triggered by human activity such as river pollution or global warming. Whatever the cause, time will be needed for nature to do her bit and repair the damage.

Resource 1.6 shows more people. Where would you fit them onto the timescale chart?

9. Study the timescales in **Resource 1.5** and **Resource 1.6**. Discuss with your teacher what each type of timescale is like. Draw a line 20 cm long and plot these timescales on that line. Make sure that they are drawn at an appropriate scale to one another. What are the differences between the timescales?

RESOURCE 1.6 Timescales.

0 — DAILY HUMAN TIMESCALE — 24 HOURS

0 — INCOME TIMESCALE — 4 WEEKS

As long as my salary gets transferred into my account each month I can pay my mortgage

0 — COMPANY TIMESCALE — 12 MONTHS

0 — ELECTORAL TIMESCALE — 5 YEARS

0 — HUMAN LIFE TIMESCALE — 100 YEARS

0 — ECOLOGICAL TIMESCALE — 1000 YEARS

0 — GEOLOGICAL TIMESCALE — MILLIONS OF YEARS

RESOURCE 1.7
Table of events.

Event	Scale	Estimated recovery time
Ice Age		
Hurricane		
Volcanic eruption		
Flood		
Drought		
Rise in sea level		
Global warming		
Avalanche		
Forest destruction		
Earthquake		
Bushfire		
River pollution		
Ozone depletion		
Acid rain		

10. Look at **Resource 1.7**. This table lists a variety of events. Each one has an impact on the environment to a greater or lesser degree. Using the table fill in the blank columns. For *Scale* consider whether the event would have been local, regional, national, continental or global.
    For *Estimated Recovery Time* remember this is NOT how long it lasts but how long it would take a system to recover. Choose from: 5 years, human lifetime, ecological lifetime (100s–1000s of years), geological lifetime (millions of years).
11. What do you notice about events and recovery times? What principles should humans apply when we make plans to use natural resources and ecosystems?

Humans have been around for a short period of time but there are many activities that we are involved in that have an impact on the environment. We have to understand the complexity of time and systems. It is essential that we are SUSTAINABLE and allow systems TIME to recover. For instance the chopping down of the rainforests is an issue that even your teachers and parents were taught about when they were at school yet we are still chopping them down and moving on when the system fails us. This is because we do not allow enough time for it to RECOVER. For the time being we are confined to 'Spaceship Earth', so we must protect what we have.

Sustainable development

What does **sustainability** mean? The following three definitions have been suggested by various groups.

1. 'Sustainable development is development that meets the needs of the present without compromising the ability of future generations to meet their own needs.' (Bruntland Report)
2. 'Sustainable development means improving the quality of life while living within the carrying capacity of supporting ecosystems.' (World Wide Fund for Nature (WWF))
3. 'A sustainable planet is contingent on world peace, respect for human rights, participatory democracy, self-determination of peoples, respect for indigenous peoples, their land, religion and culture and the protection of all species.' (Women's Action, Agenda 21)

Work in a small group to complete the following tasks. For this

12. Discuss the three definitions of 'Sustainable development' with your group. Define the following terms
- human rights
- participatory democracy
- self determination
- indigenous.

13. Using resources in your library, CD Roms and books find out some information about the following: **a)** The Bruntland Report; **b)** World Wide Fund for Nature (WWF); **c)** Agenda 21.

i) What are they?

ii) What do they have in common?

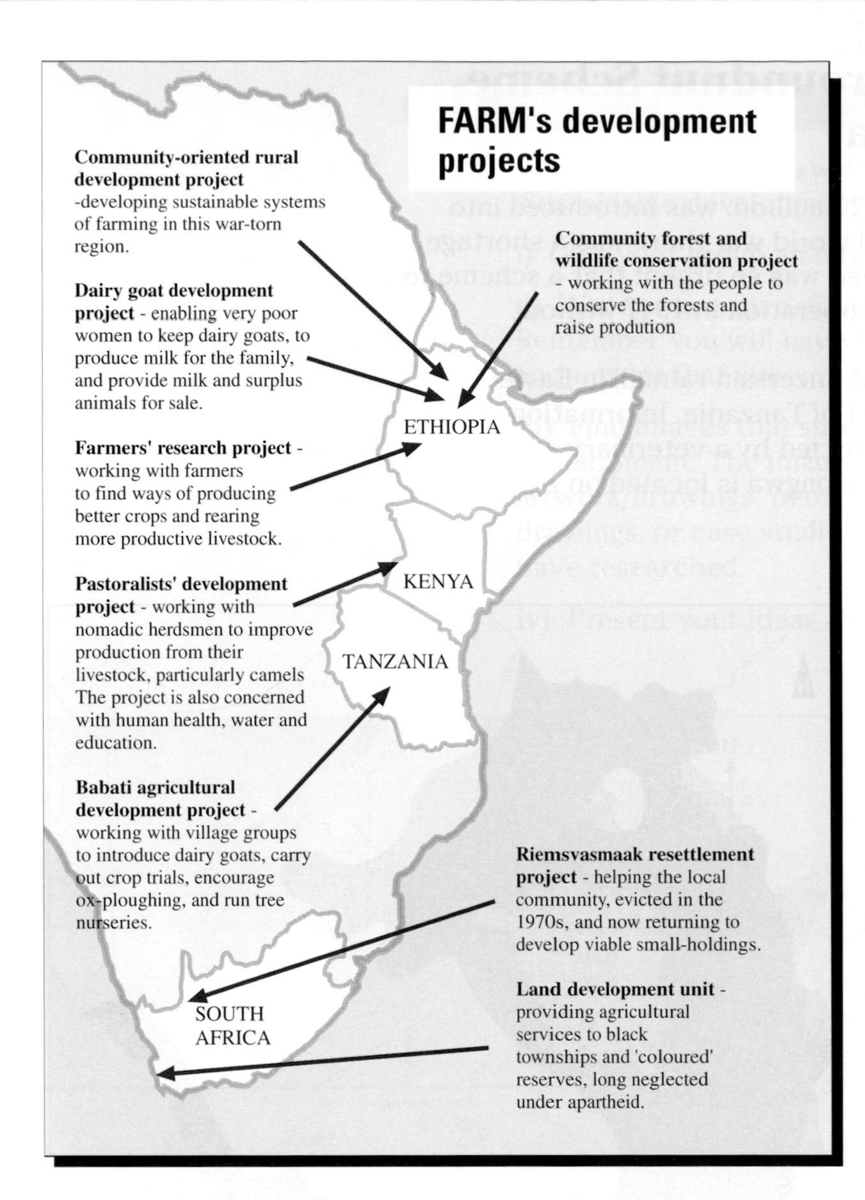

RESOURCE 1.10 Map of FARM's development projects.

Case Study 2: Dairy Goat Development Project

Resource 1.11 shows Halima and her family. She and her husband are farmers. She lives with her family of five children in the village of Awbere, in Ethiopia. They work hard to farm a small plot of land, but like many others find it increasingly difficult to produce enough food for their family. Prior to FARM's involvement, they had no animals.

RESOURCE 1.11 Halima and her family.

Food and Agriculture Research Management Ltd, or FARM, is a charity that helps farmers in Africa grow more food to feed their families and to sell at market. It aims to promote sustainability and environmentally friendly projects. They helped Halima with a Dairy Goat Programme which is beginning to change her life. The project initially lent her two goats and taught her how to grow their fodder on waste land. With regular nourishing food the goats produce more milk that Halima and her family can use. She also has a regular supply of manure for her crops. A good pedigree billy goat was used to breed with her goats and she now has a herd that produces even more milk which she can sell at a local market. She has been able to pay back FARM the cost of the goats, and she is now in a better position to sustain herself and her family.

FARM run projects all over Africa. **Resource 1.10** shows the things they do. They aim to tackle the problems of poverty from the bottom up. Halima had a small amount of assistance to start with and she now can run the project herself, earn some money and educate others to help themselves.

Average sustainability score

In this activity you will find out the average sustainability score for each case study and make a comparison of the two figures. In order to compare schemes we often need to use a scoring system. In this case you will be using the *Average Sustainability Score (ASS)*. Carefully study the two case studies. To calculate the Average Sustainability Score for each case study you must follow these steps:

15. **Resource 1.12** overleaf lists the categories which we use to assess sustainability. Each has a question attached to it which will help you as you analyse the schemes. You must give a score to each scheme for each category. The scores range from 1 to 5. 1 is the least sustainable, 5 is the most sustainable. Fill in these scores on the table.
16. Add all of the scores together for each scheme and put the total in the total box.
17. Divide the totals by the total number of categories. Put this in the appropriate box. You now have the Average Sustainability Score for each scheme.
18. Answer the following questions

    i) What is the Average Sustainability Score for each Scheme?

    ii) Which scheme is MOST sustainable?

    iii) What are the main differences between the two schemes?

    iv) Give reasons for these differences.
19. Using the information from this activity add information to the poster you produced in Activity 13, part iv, to give examples of schemes that help illustrate your definition.

These two schemes had different approaches to development, which reflected on their success. One of the schemes saw people as being part of the environment, whilst the other saw people as being outside of the environment. We do something to the environment, then sit back and expect it to change in a certain way (inside the environment, which is 'not part of us'), or we introduce the scheme into the environment, which we, are part of, realising that the scheme must not only not harm the other parts of the environment, but that it must also be capable of lasting.

Category	Question	Case Study 1	Case Study 2
Environmental Knowledge	How much research and planning appeared to be put in before the scheme went ahead?		
Time	Planners are often in a hurry for results. Is there evidence of beginning the project too soon?		
Money	Development plans can cost millions of pounds. This amount of money often has to come from abroad. Is there any evidence in these cases that money came from abroad?		
Know How	Is there evidence of lack of know how and qualified people to investigate and maintain the plan?		
Change	People often dislike change. Is there any evidence that the scheme will involve drastic change?		
Ownership of land	Are there problems of ownership of the land?		
Local conditions	It is important to work with local conditions. Is there evidence to suggest that natural factors such as weather and soil may be a hazard?		
Type of Scheme	Is the scheme top down (bosses telling people what to do) or bottom up (local people involved at each stage)? Is there communication and consultation?		
Scale	Is it large scale or small scale? Is that scale suited to the local situation and the needs of the people?		
Environment	Is the scheme environmentally friendly or not?		
	TOTAL		
	Divided by no. Categories		

RESOURCE 1.12
Checklist for assessing sustainability.

There are many examples of sustainable development schemes from the past, some of which occurred by accident. We are more aware of the need for sustainability now, and perhaps have more technology to help us get there, BUT there are equally many clearly unsustainable schemes which are still being pursued today (some examples appear later in this book), and *it is this which is more worrying*!

WHAT MOTHER EARTH THROWS UP!!

2

Key Idea

In this chapter we will be examining the world of earthquakes and volcanoes, where these natural phenomena occur in the world, what causes them, what happens and our responses to them?

Imagery

Today imagery is a big part of our lives. Advertisers are always seeking new ways to present their products. **Resource 2.1** shows an image which is used by advertisers to promote the Frontera.

RESOURCE 2.1
Frontera advertisement.

1. Using the information from the advert in **Resource 2.1**, write 4 facts about volcanoes and then list features that seem to be equivalent in the Frontera advertisement.
2. **i)** What is cataclysmic about volcanoes and earthquakes?
   ii) Why have the advertisers chosen to use volcanic activity as a method to promote the Frontera?

Blowing your top

WHAT IS A VOLCANO?

Volcanic activity is the result of tectonic processes that take place beneath the Earth's surface. The Earth's crust is broken up into a number of pieces called plates. Volcanoes are usually found at the edges of these plates. A Volcano is a crack in the crust through which comes lava, ash, steam and gas. It has a unique structure in order to allow the escape of magma from the mantle beneath. **Resource 2.2** shows the basic structure of a volcano. Lava collects in the magma chamber and when pressure is great enough the volcano erupts.

Resource 2.3 shows two main types of volcano: shield and composite. Shield volcanoes have thin runny lava and gentle slopes. Composite cones are more violent when they erupt, blasting lava out through the vent which settles as ash: new lava then pours over this and layers are built up as the process repeats. **Resource 2.4** summarises the characteristics of these volcanoes.

RESOURCE 2.2
Structure of a volcano.

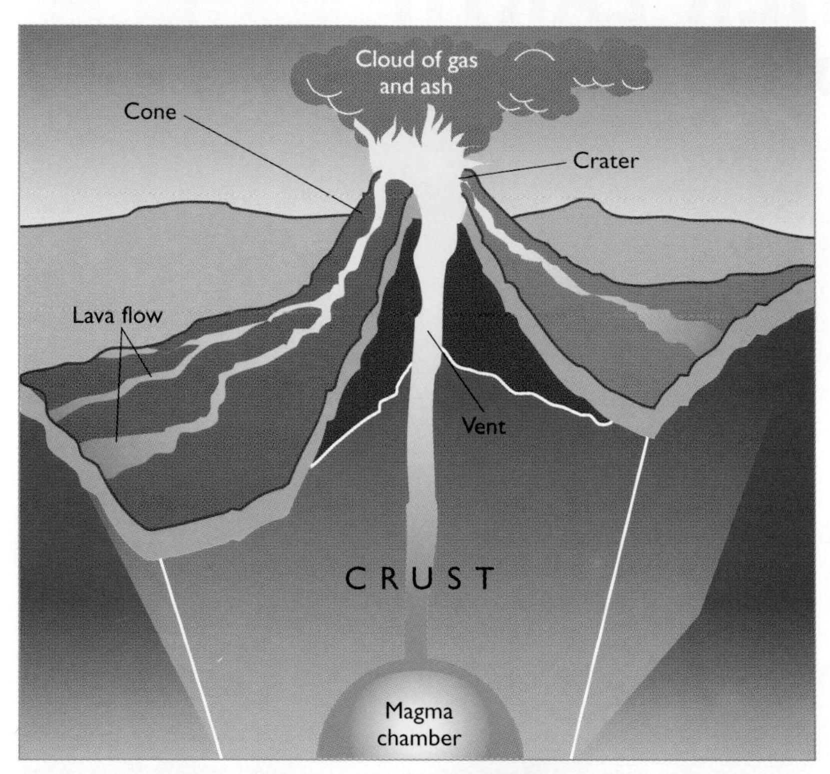

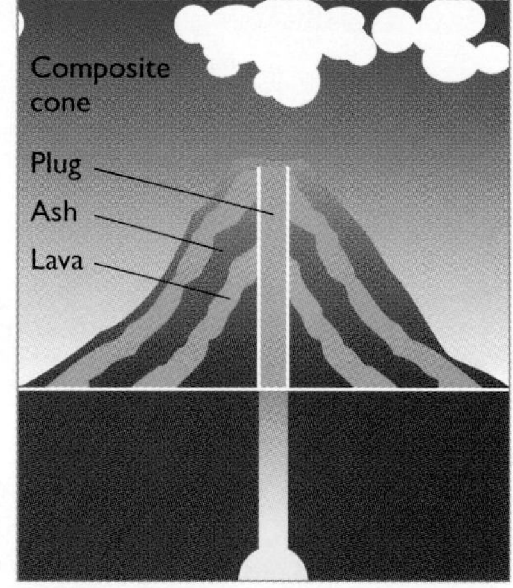

RESOURCE 2.3
2 types of volcano.

RESOURCE 2.4
Characteristics of shield and composite volcanoes.

	Shield	Composite
types of plate	constructive	destructive
areas found	rift valley, ocean ridges	coastal mountain
landscape	broad low volcano	high steep sided
lava	Silica-poor (e.g. basalt)	Silica-rich (e.g. rhyolite)
eruption	flows over crater	violent, sudden, throws upward

Cracking up

WHAT ARE EARTHQUAKES?

Earthquakes are the result of a **shock wave** passing through the ground. The source of the earthquake is called the **focus**. This may be at some depth in the crust (for shallow earthquakes) or deeper into the mantle (for intermediate and deep earthquakes which are more powerful). The **Epicentre** is the place on the earth's surface immediately above the focus. Rings or contours of shock waves, called **isoseismal lines**, with decreasing powers of destruction radiate out across the surface from the epicentre. **Resource 2.5** summarises the structure of an earthquake.

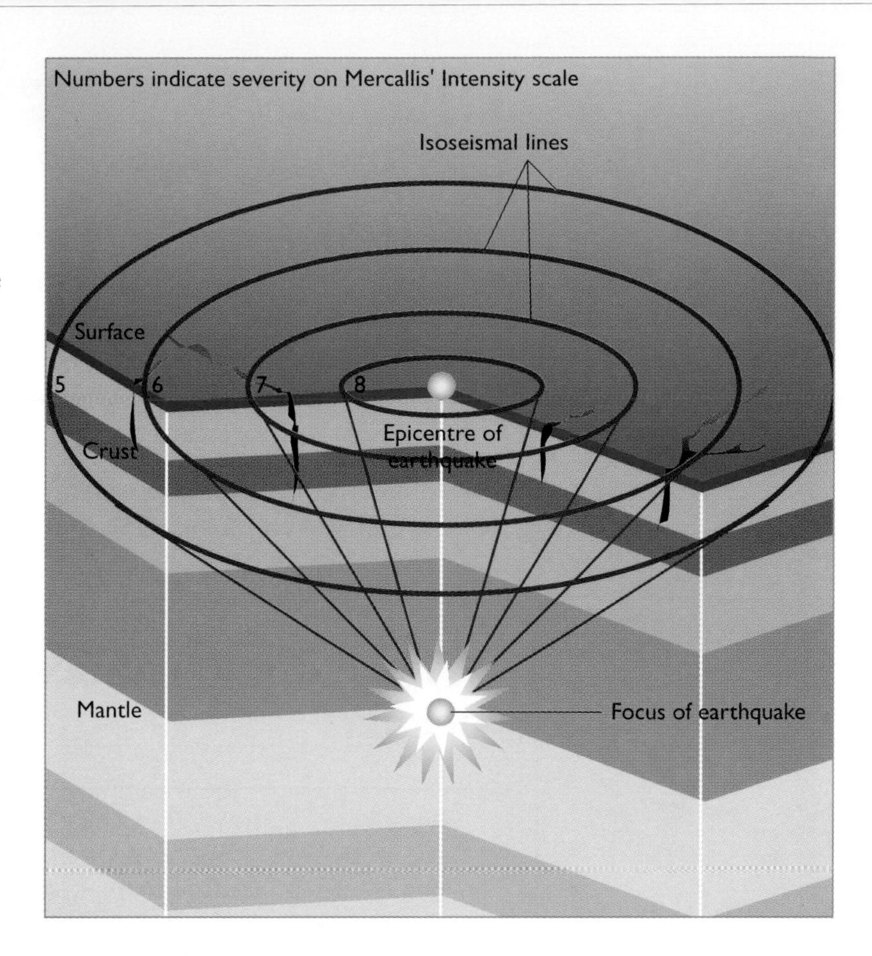

RESOURCE 2.5
Structure of an earthquake.

MEASURING EARTHQUAKES

Earthquakes are measured using two scales: the Richter Scale measures intensity, the Mercalli Scale measures magnitude. Both are named after the scientists who devised them. The Richter scale helps us assess the damage caused by an earthquake while the Mercalli scale is a measure of the energy released by an earthquake when the rocks snap apart. Resource 2.6 shows how these scales are graded against what actually happens.

Mercalli	Description	Richter
1		0
2	slight tremor	3.5
3		4.2
4	windows rattle	4.3
5		4.8
6	cupboards fall, trees sway	4.9
7		5.5
8	chimneys fall, roads crack	6.2
9		6.9
10	houses fall, huge cracks in ground	7.0
11		7.4
12	everything is destroyed	8.9

RESOURCE 2.6
Mercalli and Richter Scales.

3. Major earthquakes have occurred in recent years in America, Japan and India. Using books in your library or a CD Rom find out the following:
   i) Where in each country the earthquake happened?
   ii) When they occurred?
   iii) How much they measured on the Richter scale?
   iv) How many people died as a result?
4. Why do you think an earthquake usually causes more damage and loss of life than a volcano?

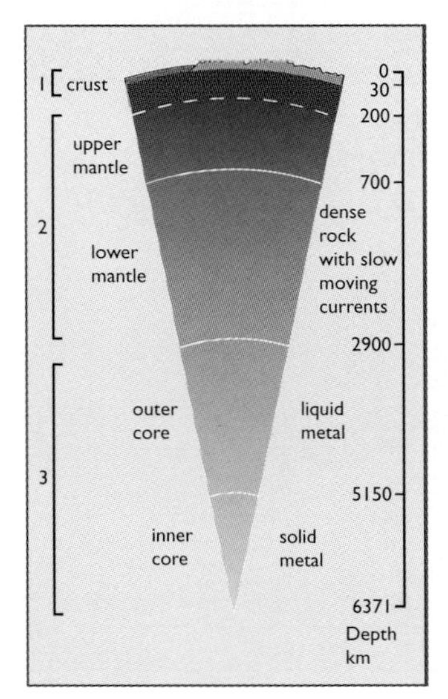

RESOURCE 2.7
Segments of the earth.

Where do volcanoes and earthquakes occur?

Resource 2.7 shows that the earth is made up of three main layers: **the crust**, **the mantle** and **the core**. The crust is solid rock while the mantle is formed of thick molten rock and the core is made up of layers of liquid rock, liquid metal and solid metal. The crust is the thinnest of these layers and broken into plates which move on the currents of molten rock. Where these plates butt against each other there is often stress: some plates are moving towards each other, some are pulling apart, some sliding past each other in opposite directions. It is at these plate boundaries that volcanoes and earthquakes occur most often.

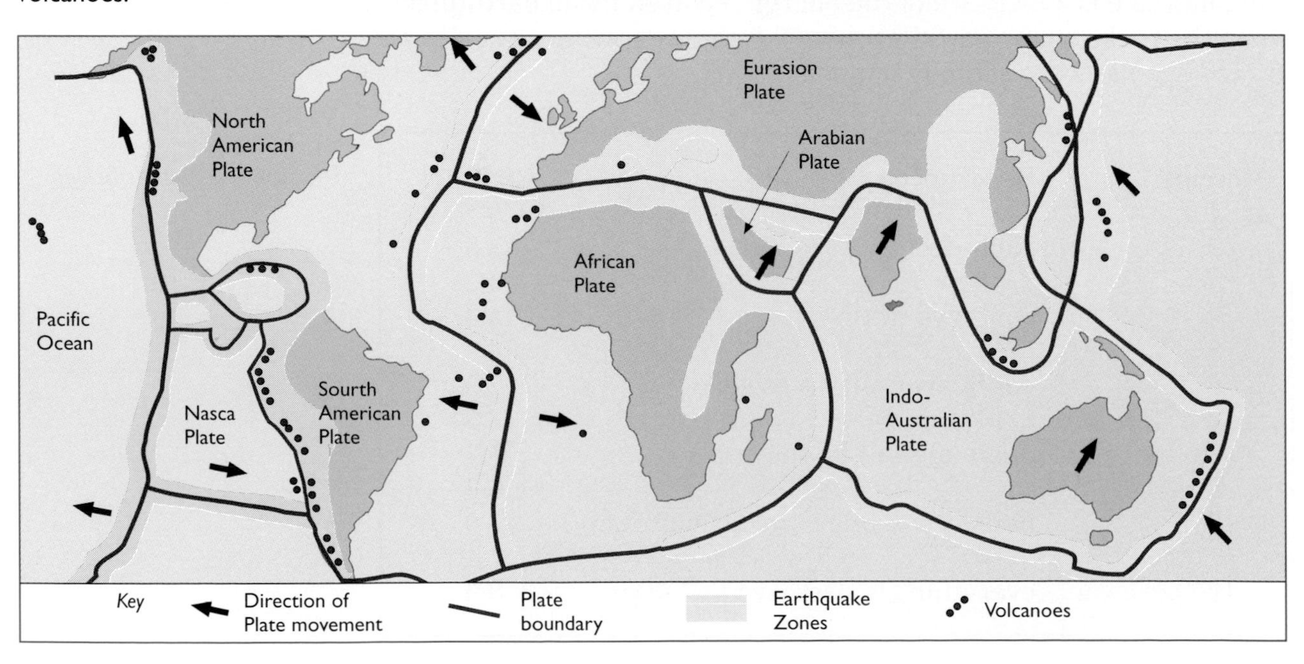

RESOURCE 2.8
Plates, earthquakes and volcanoes.

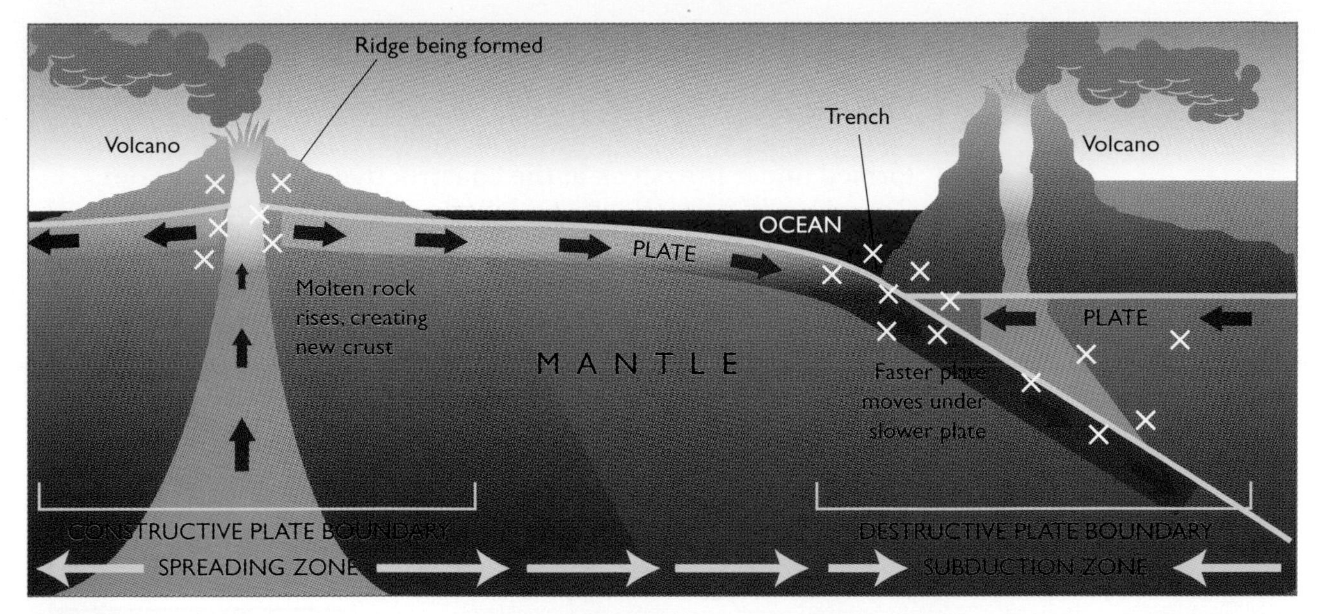

RESOURCE 2.9
Constructive and destructive plates.

Resource 2.9 shows two main types of plate movement. Constructive plate boundaries are where plates pull apart and often new crust forms in a ridge. This is taking place under the Atlantic ocean in the mid-oceanic ridge. The earth's crust is stretching here. At destructive plate boundaries, the crust is 'eaten' as one plate moves under another. Here massive earthquakes and volcanoes can occur as happens in the Pacific rim or Ring of Fire.

RESOURCE 2.10
Types of plate boundaries.

conservative	touch each other but no movement
sliding past	each slide in opposite directions past each other
constructive	new crust is built up as plates pull apart
destructive	one plate is consumed sliding beneath another

5. Explain why you think most earthquakes and volcanoes happen near plate boundaries.
6. Using Resource 2.10 label the types of plate boundaries on Resource 2.8.

   i) Which do you think are the most dangerous and why?

   ii) Using Resource 2.3 what sorts of volcanoes do you think occur most often at constructive plate boundaries? What sort might be found more often at destructive plate boundaries?
7. On Resource 2.9 label the earthquakes (marked by X) that are shallow and those that are deep. What do you think is causing the deep, more violent earthquakes?

CASE STUDY: THE ATLANTIC

The Atlantic is 200 million years old. Yet geologists call it a young ocean. And it is growing all the time. New crust is being formed under the ocean at the constructive plate boundaries. Occasionally transatlantic telephone cables snap because of this widening process. The age of ocean crust can be measured and the pattern of ageing and spreading is a distinctive one. We can use information like this to see how fast plates are moving and changing in order to assess what may happen in the future.

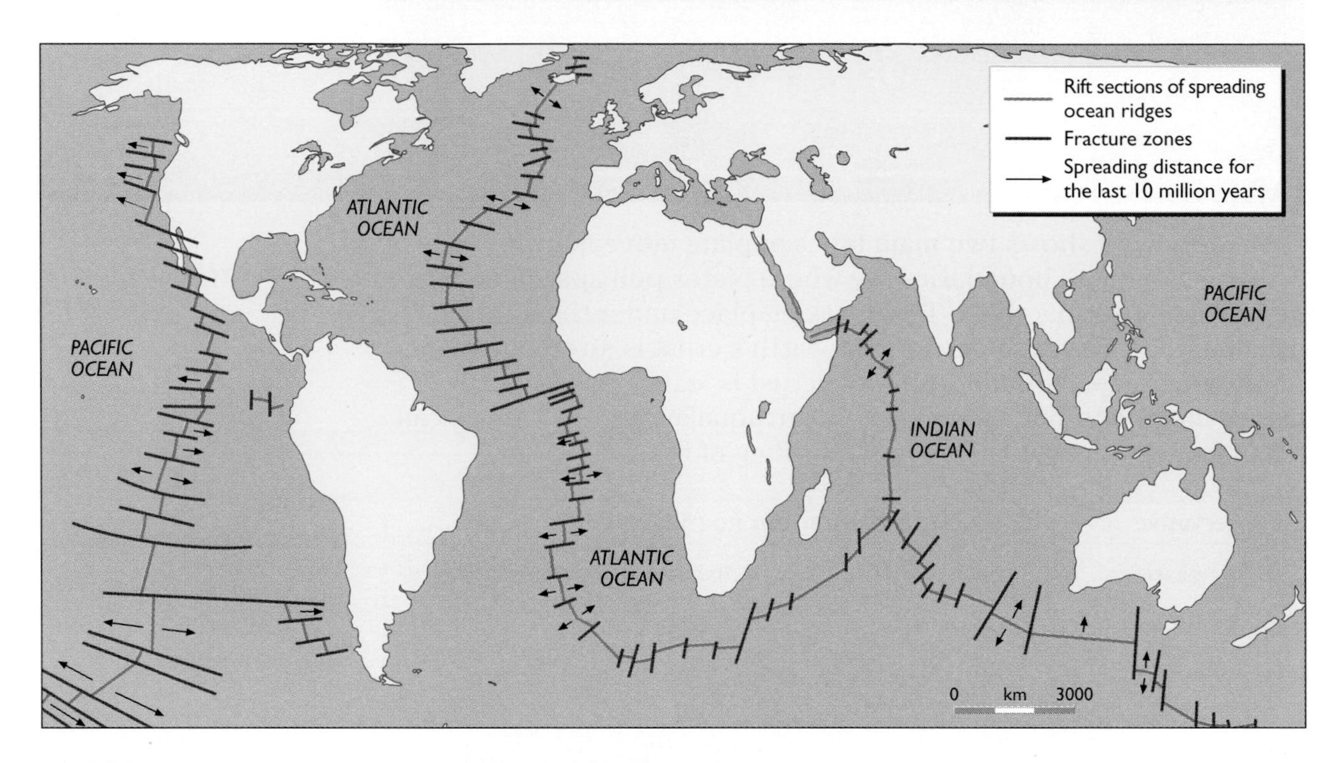

RESOURCE 2.11
Rift section of spreading ocean ridges.

8. Using **Resource 2.11** describe the pattern of ageing of ocean crust in the North Atlantic. Approximately how many millions of years does it take for 100 km of new ocean crust to form?
9. Where is new ocean crust forming in the Atlantic? Use the key and scale to estimate spreading distance of new crust in the Atlantic for the last 10 million years.
10. Where is the greatest rate of ocean floor spreading in the world? Approximately what width of new crust has been created in the last 10 million years there?
11. The earth is not getting any bigger. So if new crust is being created in certain parts of the earth, suggest what must be happening in other parts?

Impacts on humans

Earthquakes and volcanoes have an impact on people's lives in many different ways. They can be extremely destructive as with the earthquake in Mexico City. But they can sometimes be positive, as with the Case Study below, Montanas de Fuego, where the natural energy source is used as a tourist attraction, bringing jobs and money to the area. Look in any newspaper for any year and you will find records of earthquakes and volcanoes. Over the centuries we have learnt more about these natural hazards, investing money in researching how we can minimise the negative impact of these events and exploit the positive impacts.

Case Study 'Montanas de Fuego'

LOCATION

This amazing volcanic landscape is located in the South West of the island of Lanzarote, the most easterly of the Spanish Canary Islands. Resource 2.12 shows the location of the 'Montanas de Fuego' (Mountains of Fire) in the Timanfaya National Park.

LANDSCAPE

The area was covered with volcanic debris during the six years of volcanic eruptions which took place between 1730 and 1736. The evidence of this activity is the immense sea of lava and about 30 major volcanic cones. There are also many smaller cones called 'hornitos'. The landscape is littered with lava rocks. There is a very specialised plant and animal life that exists in this dry, burnt out environment where very little rain falls. Some rushes flourish along with 200 species of colourful lichen. The Haria Lizard along with 87 varieties of birdlife have been recorded.

RESOURCE 2.12
Canary Islands and Timanfaya National Park.

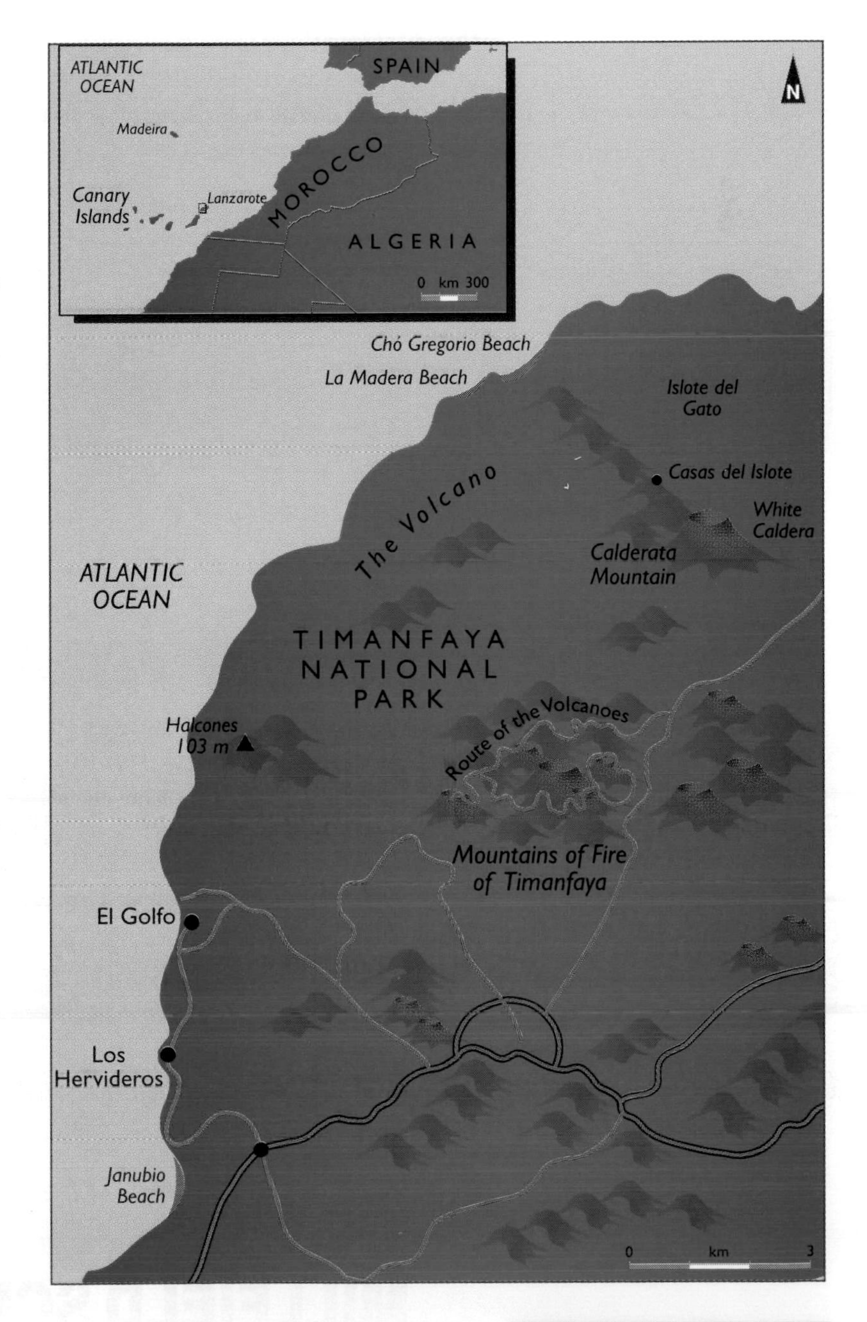

THE NATIONAL PARK

On 9th August, 1974 the 'Parque Nacional De Timanfaya' (Timanfaya National Park) was created. It does not protect endangered species, but is a mineral museum (Resource 2.12): volcanic cones, craters, seas of lava, ash, tongues of liquid magma, now solidified into natural monuments.

TOURIST ACTIVITY

To highlight the productivity of such environments there are unique tourist activities. How would you like to eat chicken cooked on a natural Bar-B-Q? Tourists are directed to 'Islote de Hilario' (Hilario's Place). It is named after a shepherd who lived on his own there for many years! Now there is a restaurant that not only offers views of the surrounding area but cooks food placed over a deep volcanic chasm. Geothermal heat rises from the bowels of the volcano. Just below the surface temperatures reach 100°C whilst at 10 m below the surface they reach 600°C.

Calling upon all young devils who visit this restaurant! I want all visits to my restaurant to be an enjoyable and also an educational experience. So many people believe that volcanoes are dangerous. I want to tell the other side of the story – that there are positive impacts – I need you to help me advertise this.

RESOURCE 2.13
Proprietor of 'El Diablo'.

12. Design an attractive leaflet for 'El Diablo' that can be placed in a pack of tourist information and displayed at strategic locations around the island. Your leaflet should include:
    - Maps showing people how to get to the restaurant.
    - A description of the type of landscape visitors will be able to see
    - An explanation of how this landscape is formed.
    - A section on 'How my restaurant works'.

    It is important that the information you give is factual, presented well and will encourage tourists to come here to sample the delicacies. Remember that people will need to be convinced that it is a good thing and they will not need to fear for their lives!!

Different countries – different responses

Different countries respond in different ways to natural hazards. Some countries have the money to invest in research and prepare people for such an event. In others, where towns and cities are overcrowded and badly planned, an earthquake can cause more damage but there is very little money to help ease the situation.

RESOURCE 2.14
Average number of deaths by earthquake.

Country	Number of Earthquakes etc	Number of people killed	Number of deaths per disaster
Japan 1960–1981	43	2 700	?
Peru 1960–1981	31	91 000	?

13. Using Resource 2.14 complete the last column by calculating the number of deaths per disaster.
14. Using the information in this section describe the differences between the number of people killed by earthquakes in Japan compared to the number of people killed by earthquakes in Peru.
15. State what types of country Japan and Peru are and suggest reasons why such differences occur between these two types.

RESOURCE 2.15
Map of Pacific Earthquake Zone.

Predicting the big one

Today it is taken for granted that weather can be forecast and we can prepare if we know it is likely to snow or become a heat wave. Prediction is one of the most important ways to reduce the impacts of earthquakes and volcanoes. If prepared for these events, people can be evacuated before it happens. Road, bridges and buildings in areas prone to these events can be strengthened. However, prediction is very difficult even for the experts.

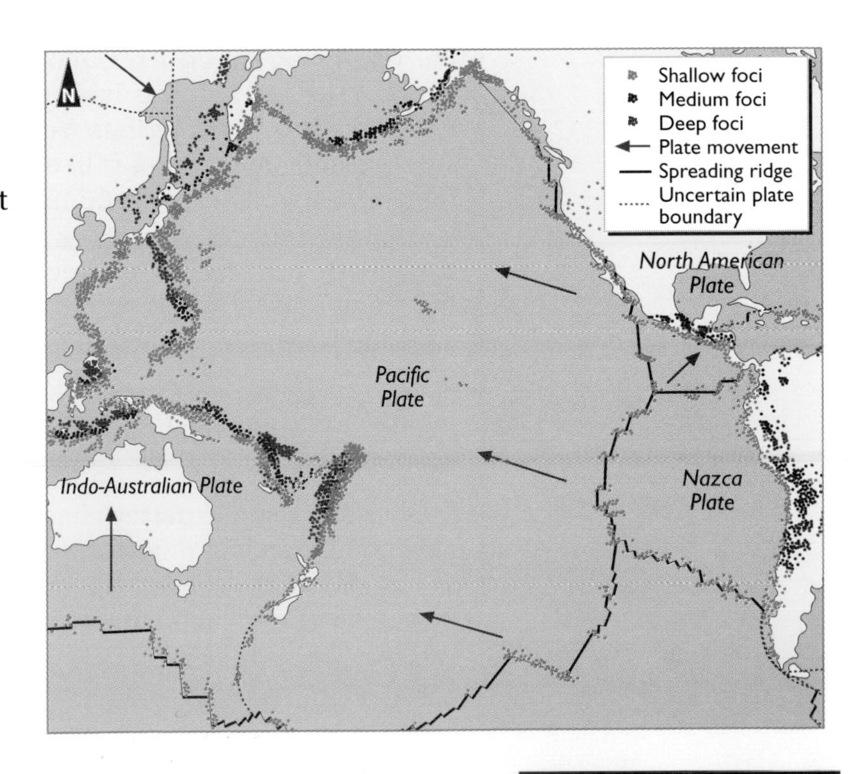

16. You are going to be cast in the role of chief vulcanologist for the US geological survey, absorbing the latest information on the Pinatubo volcano in the Philippines and deciding what warning, if any, to give to the governments and the public.

Pinatubo lies 90 km NW of Manila, the capital of the Philippines. It provides a home for the largest US bases abroad, home to 20 000 American service personnel in the Airforce and Navy.

Familiarise yourselves with the four levels of alertness used to warn people of perceived levels of impending danger.

Alert level 1 Concern expressed about volcanic unrest.
Alert level 2 Processes are underway that could culminate in eruptive activity.
Alert level 3 A life or property threatening volcanic event is imminent.
Alert level 4 – GET OUT – EVACUATE

As you read the diary of events you will provide advice bulletins which state the alert level you have decided. Pay attention to the actual geography of the area: if you decide evacuations are necessary, you need to pinpoint which settlements you mean, and how far away and in which direction they must go.

DIARY OF EVENTS

Early May You set up 7 seismic stations. These now tell you that some of the earthquakes have their foci 5 miles beneath the volcano – this looks serious! You are also now measuring sulphur dioxide emissions. In early May, the readings show 500 tonnes/day, which is substantial. By the end of the month it is 5000 tonnes/day. So, it is not a local tectonic event; it must be magma. BUT, Pinatubo has been dormant for centuries. Could the magma rise, then stop? (this is common). But of course infrequent eruptions often mean violent ones. *What is your advice?*

3 June: A big event, a harmonic tremor, the biggest yet. *What is your advice?*

5 June: The seismic pattern has changed; the earthquakes are now coming from a different side of the mountain. Plus the system is not degassing any longer. There is a blob or spine of new magma showing. *What is your advice?*

You meet U.S. Commander who says they are not ready to leave yet. More steam is seen emerging. The seismic sheet, which makes a continuous recording of the tremors, goes from –v–v– to VVVVVVVVV . . . a local event? This sometimes goes back down, but could also be the volcano 'cranking up'! *What is your advice?*

7 June: A dome is seen inside the crater: a little slug of cold magma. *What is your advice?*

12–14 June: Two more days of early eruptions, sending ash and sand showers up to 50 miles away. What's keeping the lid on?! A major typhoon hits the area at speeds up to 200 kph at the same time to add to the problem. What is your advice?

15 June: ERUPTION! The big one! An ash cloud at day-break 100 000 feet in the air, 10 miles wide. 15 miles away it dominates the horizon. Hot ash flows roar down in all directions. At 6.0 a.m. an explosion, lightning from its own weather system, then the typhoon hits at 6.30 a.m. It is dark like night. You can't see or hear. It's scary. It is raining big pumice balls, 2–6" across. At 1.45 p.m. a big blast: your instrument sites ceased to function, knocked out by the ash bombs. Your advice? . . .

THE WARNINGS THAT THE U.S. GEOLOGICAL SURVEY TEAM ACTUALLY MADE

(for comparison with *your* warnings)

3 June: Alert level 2 declared. 20 000 people evacuated from the closest villages.

Early on 5 June: The team was 'leaning towards alert level 3, with an expectation of eruption within 2 weeks'. They realised they would only have one chance to evacuate on time.

Late on 5 June: Reluctantly, the team 'call a 4'. All were evacuated in a 12 mile radius. 120 000 people left their homes for shelters.

12 June: The team was 'awed by the first big blast!'. They felt 'emotional relief that they had really nailed it'.

15 June: The U.S. Base felt it was 'time to leave', so with pumice balls bouncing off their cars, they mounted an orderly retreat. Thanks to their predictions (and yours?!) virtually all were evacuated safely. BUT the blast and the typhoon spread devastation. Angeles and Olongapo towns were covered in ash and suffered roof collapse. The death toll was kept to under 500 due to the prediction.

It's only natural

Earthquakes and volcanic activity are natural phenomena. We have to learn to live with them and their impacts. They are only hazards because we make them out to be so. Despite destruction people still live near volcanoes and in earthquake zones. This is for a variety of reasons: they may not be able to afford to move; the soil may be very fertile; sulphur created by an eruption can be extracted and used. So humans adapt to living there and accept these hazards as part of the system they live in.

Case Study: Stromboli – A Volcano

Stromboli is a volcano found in the Tyrrhenian Sea. Resource 2.16 shows that it is part of a group of volcanic islands known as the Lipari Islands, off NE Sicily. Stromboli is known for its continuous volcanic activity. Volcanologists (people who study volcanoes) use the term 'strombolian' to describe persistent volcanic activity.

RESOURCE 2.16
Map of SW Italy.

RESOURCE 2.17
Stromboli.

17. Study Resource 2.17 carefully.

    i) Draw a sketch of the volcano.

    ii) Select TWO colours. Colour 1 is for PHYSICAL features
    Colour 2 is for HUMAN features.

    On your sketch add labels to show both physical and human features.

18. Describe what you think the effect of constant volcanic activity is on the people who live there? Why do you think they stay?

ENERGY – MAY THE FORCE BE WITH YOU!

3

Key Idea

In this chapter, we will explore the concept of energy, the importance it plays in your life and the responsibility we have to ensure sustainable energy sources as well as careful maintenance of the environment.

RESOURCE 3.1 Differents sorts of energy through time.

> 'Amidst these flaming, smoky clanging works, I beheld the remains of what had once been happy farmhouses, now ruined and deserted. The ground beneath them had sunk by the working of the coal. . . . They had, in former times, been surrounded by clumps of trees, but only the skeletons of them remained. The grass had been parched by the vapours of sulphurous acid, and every herbaceous object was of a ghastly grey.'
>
> *James Nasmyth in 1883.*

James Nasmyth was an inventor during the Industrial Revolution. He was appalled by what happened to the Black Country as factories grew. How much real progress have we made since 1883? Remember that with our increasing technological ability has come an increase in our potential to harm the environment. We also have the ability to use our knowledge to develop energy sources to sustain the environment.

Carefully read the following statements:

(i) The maximum daily output of a manual worker is about 0.5 kilowatt hours

(ii) The work output of a horse in an 8-hour day is 6 kilowatt-hours

(iii) A litre of petrol contains 10 kilowatt hours

1. Draw a bar chart showing the amount of energy produced by each source using the information from the statements above.

   Read the following statement:

   'The history of humanity's emergence from the lifestyle of a medium-sized foraging mammal to its present position as the earth's dominant species is one of increasing skill at harnessing and manipulating energy.'

2. Using the information in **Resource 3.1** and on your bar chart write a paragraph to show:

   i) How energy use has changed during the centuries

   ii) The importance of energy.

Everyone uses energy. We need it for many things: cooking, driving a car, lighting, heating. There are different sources of energy: some of these we are gradually using up: they are **non-renewable**. Others are renewable which means they can never be exhausted. The types of energy fall into three main categories. Coal, natural gas and oil are **fossil fuels**. They account for 83% of the world energy consumption. They are a major source of pollution as they release harmful gases into the atmosphere when burnt. As these fuels are created deep in the earth over millions of years they're non-renewable as we use them up. **Nuclear energy** forms around 5% of the world's energy. A nuclear power station is cheap to operate and creates no air pollution but it produces waste that can be harmful and is difficult and expensive to process. **Renewable energy** accounts for around 12% of the world's consumption. Wind, solar and water power are types of renewable energy.

RESOURCE 3.2
Energy portfolios.

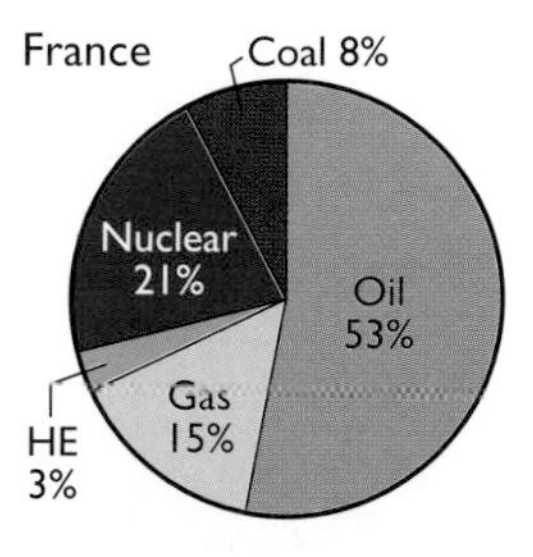

A country will meet its energy demands by using a variety of energy sources. Each country will have its own mix of different energy resources which can be called the **energy portfolio**. The energy mix of a country varies in both quality and type. Britain's energy mix is shown in **Resource 3.2** and it can be compared with those of the other countries shown. It may come as a surprise to see such variety of mixes of energy for different countries. There are special geographical, economic and political reasons for this.

Nigeria
Gas 8%
HE 2%
Oil 28%
Traditional fuels 62%

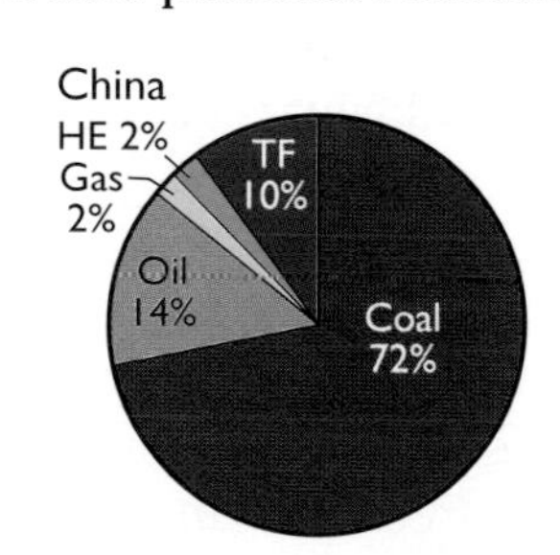

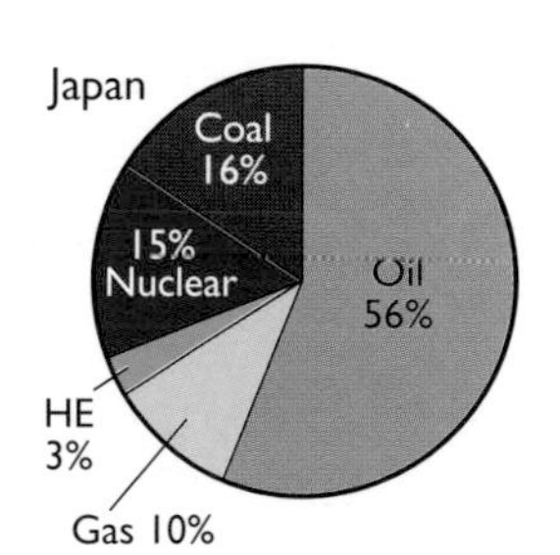

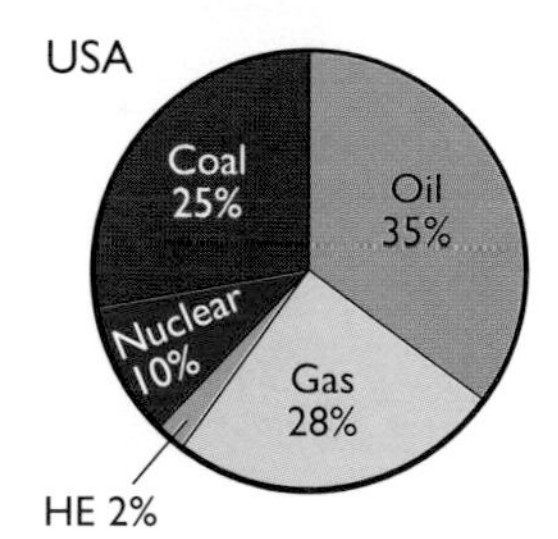

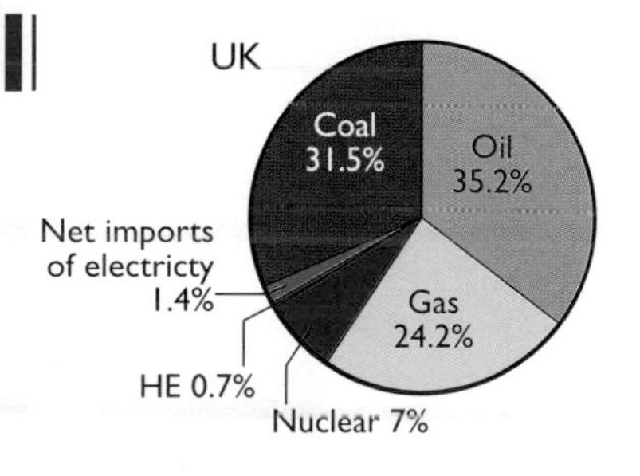

3. Using books, newspapers, CD Roms and Internet sources, describe the differences between the energy portfolios of the countries shown in **Resource 3.2**.

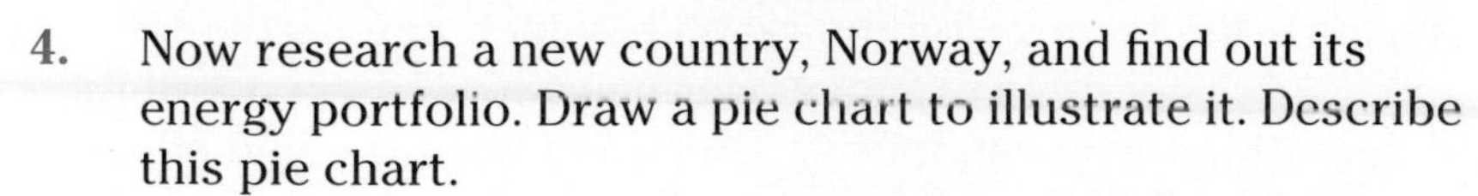

4. Now research a new country, Norway, and find out its energy portfolio. Draw a pie chart to illustrate it. Describe this pie chart.

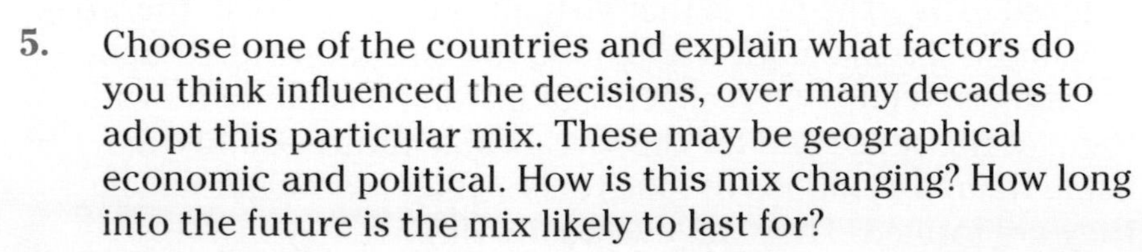

5. Choose one of the countries and explain what factors do you think influenced the decisions, over many decades to adopt this particular mix. These may be geographical economic and political. How is this mix changing? How long into the future is the mix likely to last for?

6. Using your pie charts fill in **Resource 3.3**. You will need to put the different fuel types into the three main categories in the table.

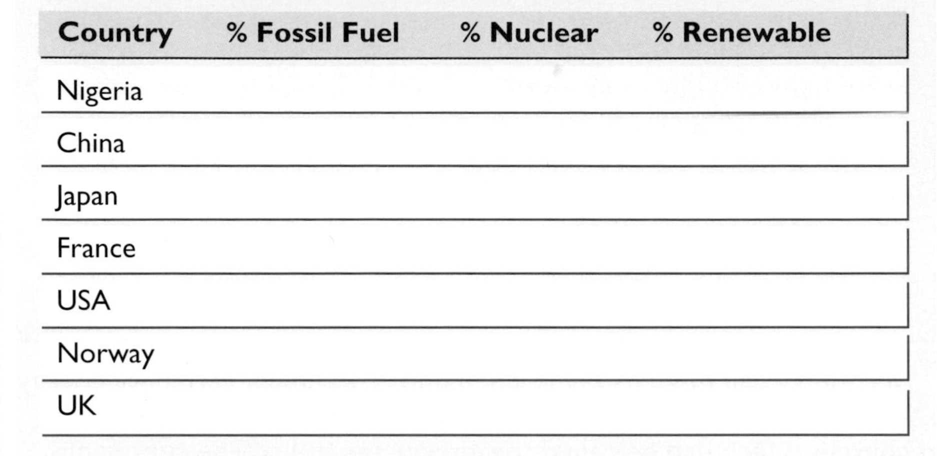

RESOURCE 3.3 Table of energy portfolios.

Country	% Fossil Fuel	% Nuclear	% Renewable
Nigeria			
China			
Japan			
France			
USA			
Norway			
UK			

RESOURCE 3.4
Triangular graph of energy mix.

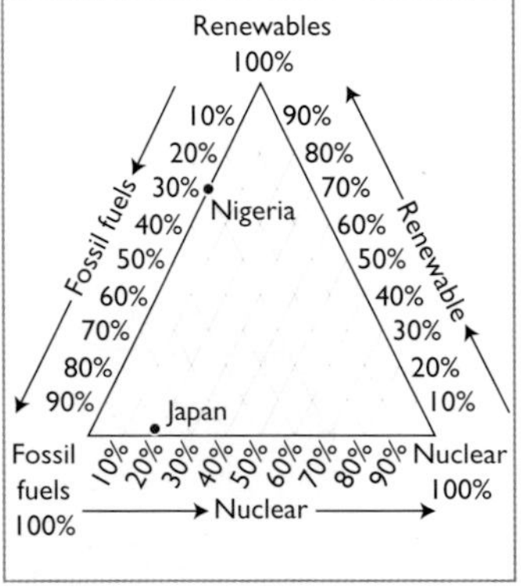

7. Consider the triangular graph (Resource 3.4). The percentages of each country's energy mix generated from these three broad categories can be used as co-ordinates to plot a dot at the position which that country occupies. Note that the three co-ordinates for one country should add up to 100%. Plot each country from your table of data, labelling each country. Japan and Nigeria have been done for you.

8. Describe the overall distribution pattern on the graph for all the countries marked. Which broad mixes of energy seem most popular? Which parts of the graph are unoccupied?

9. Study the 'Energy Risks to the Environment' graph. This is the same basic diagram as the one you have just completed. Using the information from this graph describe the range of environmental problems likely to be encountered by each of the seven countries.

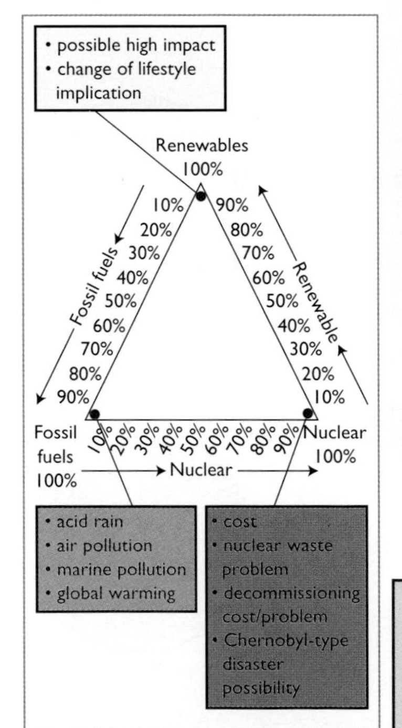

RESOURCE 3.5
Triangular graph of energy risks for the environment.

It is a fairly limited area on the graph in which any particular country can operate in or move over because of its constraints and limitations. You cannot say 'Oh I don't want the bad effects of fossil fuels'. The fact is that virtually all countries in the world are, and will remain, for a long time to come, dependent upon fossil fuels. It must be realised that it is impossible to do without them at this stage and for the foreseeable future. But we are using them up millions of times faster than the rate at which they are formed. They will eventually run out.

Pathways to consumption

It is easy to recognise the source of energy when you see logs burning on a fire: wood produces the energy and we 'consume' the heat of the fire. However, not everyone thinks about the sources of energy that produce the electricity we need to light up a light bulb.

The route that electricity takes to where it is needed, in the home, your school, to businesses is complex. At certain times of peak demand extra electricity is needed. For example on Christmas Day when people are cooking lunch or when there is a special edition of a soap on, the producers of electricity will need to ensure that there is sufficient electricity to meet the demand. Where does electricity to our homes come from and what are the problems that can occur as the electricity wends its way to your power point.

RESOURCE 3.6
Pathways of electricity 1.

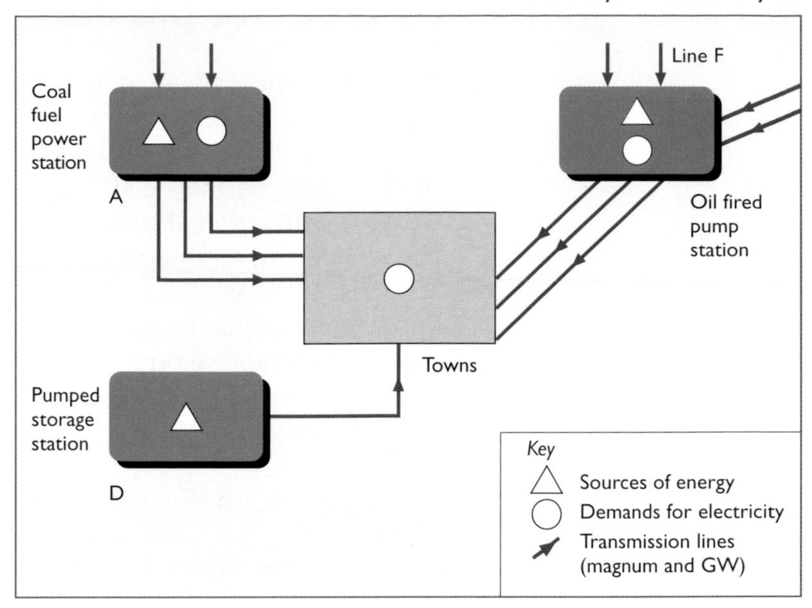

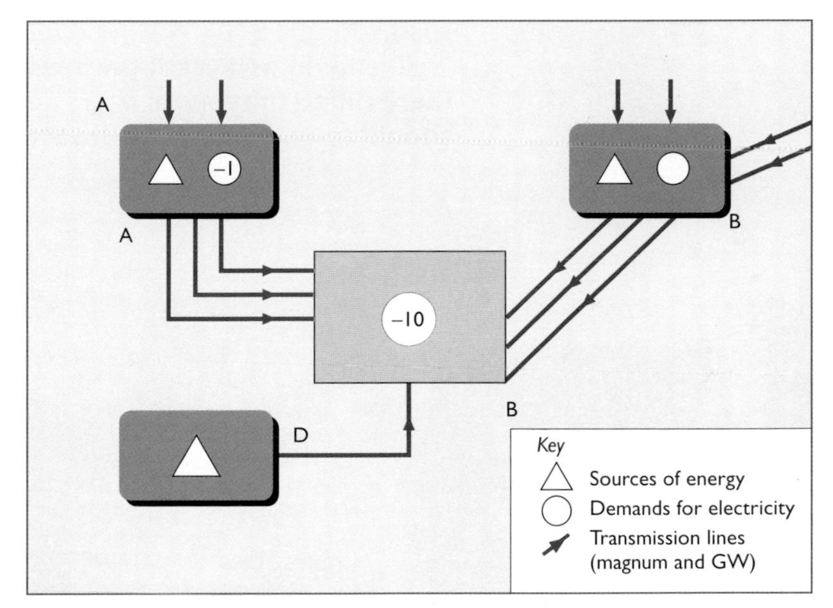

RESOURCE 3.7
Pathways of electricity 2.

10. Use **Resource 3.6** and **Resource 3.7** to answer the following questions.

i) List the sources of electricity

ii) List the places where energy is demanded

iii) What is the maximum amount of energy that can be transmitted along the power lines?

iv) What is the maximum amount of energy that can be transmitted to Town B from EACH of the sources of energy?

The car: freedom for millions . . . or a social pariah?

As we use energy we can pollute our environment. However, we cannot always simply stop using that energy source. The car has been blamed for a lot of the problems associated with the emission of CO_2. How justified is this and what is the case for the car? Governments over the next decades will be under increasing pressure from environmental groups to put the 'squeeze' on motorists. Chancellors, in Budgets, can do this by putting more tax on petrol, increasing road tax, or tax on company car users. The environmental reasons for this would not be questioned by anyone: a push to end city centre congestion and pollution is something that even the most ardent motorist would want for the sake of their children.

But putting up the price of petrol will not make a company chairperson climb out of their Jaguar and taken to a bus, yet it may confine an elderly pensioner in an outlying village to their house, because they simply cannot afford to keep their old Fiesta on the road.

So should we accept the insistence that all cars are wrong? Or are there different types of users and journeys, which the authorities should target and 'hit' with varying degrees of force?

RESOURCE 3.8 Freedom for millions?

Sonia Elliot is a single mother living in the tiny village of Great Rollright in Oxfordshire. Her car is Sonia's link with the outside world. It takes her children to school, collects the weekly shopping, and means she can get easily, cheaply and safely between home and town. She runs her car on a shoestring but *has* to have a car. There is no bus service in her remote village.

'Out here there is no alternative to the car' Sonia says. 'Of course, I must agree we must take steps to protect the environment but modern life is not that simple. I need a car and can't afford to keep paying more and more for it. There must be thousands like me who do not live in London or a city where transport alternatives are plentiful and cheap. We don't have these alternatives in the country.'

RESOURCE 3.9
Sonia Elliot.

Nick Williams-Howes drives 30 000 miles per year for his company, often from his London base for early appointments in the north of England and then cross country, arriving home late at night. His BMW is a tool of his job. Nick is always likely to be a prime budget target: a company driver, one of the elite 3 million motorists who rack up mile after mile in their luxurious paid-for cars, spewing out pollution and clogging up roads – at least, that is the picture if you believe some environmental activitists.

The myth of the company car is enduring and false: only one in ten could be regarded as a perk; for the rest the car is a mobile office doing an average 10 000 business miles, with 36% of drivers covering more than 18 000 miles a year.

Company car drivers comprise 10% of the motoring population, but account for 20% of the mileage, but company cars are usually new, with an average age of 2.6 years compared with 6.3 for a private model, therefore more fuel efficient, and less polluting. Their cars are serviced regularly, insured and taxed by employers, and increasingly, company drivers are also better trained.

Write a summary of your views on the car, stating, with reasons, which of the cases described above you most, and least, sympathise with.

'If somebody can tell me how I can do certain journeys by public transport in the time I have, then I am happy to listen' he says. 'But it just isn't possible. If I have to stay late in some towns, how can I get home? There are usually no trains to catch.'

RESOURCE 3.10
Nick Williams-Howes.

Consider these journey types:

- within-city journeys
- inter-city journeys
- rural-to-urban journeys
- urban-to-rural journeys
- within-rural journeys

11. Which of these journey types should governments clamp down on and restrict most, if they are to avoid affecting those who really need their cars? And what role can we expect improved technology to play in reducing road traffic impact on the environment?

Modern day crusaders

The case of the car reflects local impact of what is a global problem. How do we avoid polluting our environment, yet preserve quality of life? As a planet there is a common threat that faces everyone: climatic change. This is linked to the use of energy. The CO_2 emissions from our cars are having an effect on the global climate.

Men and women attend summits in order to discuss global problems and who is responsible. Climatic change is one of the key issues on their agendas.

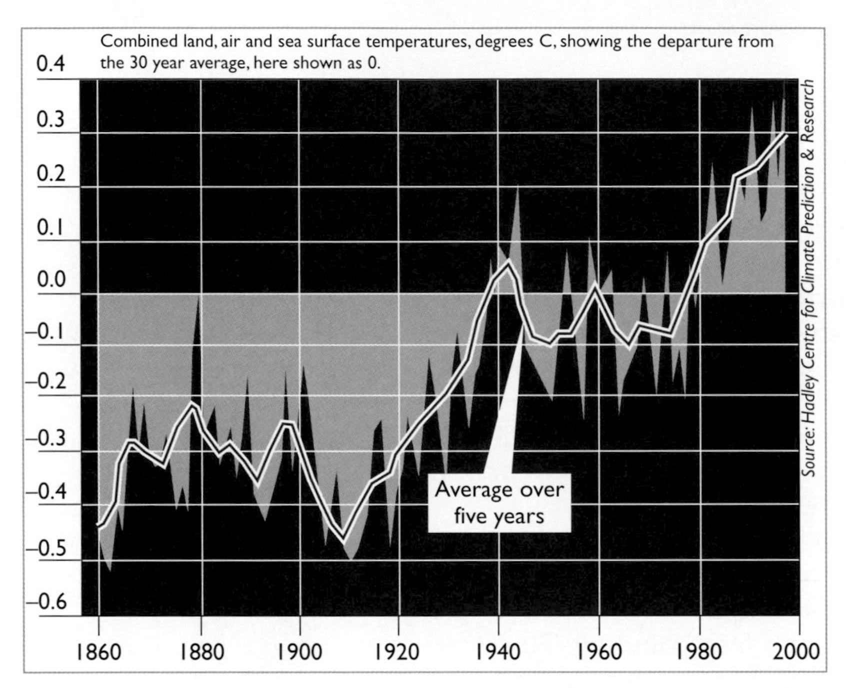

RESOURCE 3.11
Global temperatures.

The problem

Climatic change and global warming are believed to be caused by increased CO_2 emissions. **Resource 3.10** shows the global temperature change since 1960.

It is important to remember that the responsibility for the environment does not just lie with national and international organisations, but, as established through the **'Agenda 21'** framework (see Resource 4.10) set up at the Rio conference, with levels of societies including local neighbourhoods, businesses, voluntary organisations etc.

The number of cars in use worldwide is forecast to rise to 500 million by 1998, undermining international efforts to curb air pollution and halt **global warming**. Rapid economic and population growth in the developing world may dwarf our use of resources. Reports by United Nations environmental research institutes paint a gloomy picture, saying that unless there is fundamental change in energy patterns and resource consumption, global catastrophe will be here before the middle of the 21st century.

The United Nation's Food and Agriculture Organisation (FAO) claims that between 1992 and 1997 an area of forest five times the size of England has been logged or cleared in developing countries. In the Amazon region of South America, the rate of **deforestation** has risen from 11 000 km^2 a year to 15 000 km^2 during the same 5 year period. This has caused thousands of animal and plant species to become extinct, at a rate of 1–3 per hour.

About 112 billion tonnes of CO_2, the gas linked to global warming, were released into the atmosphere between 1992 and 1997. Third world debt, which it is claimed is pushing developing countries into environmentally damaging schemes rose during the same period from $1 662 billion to $2 000 billion.

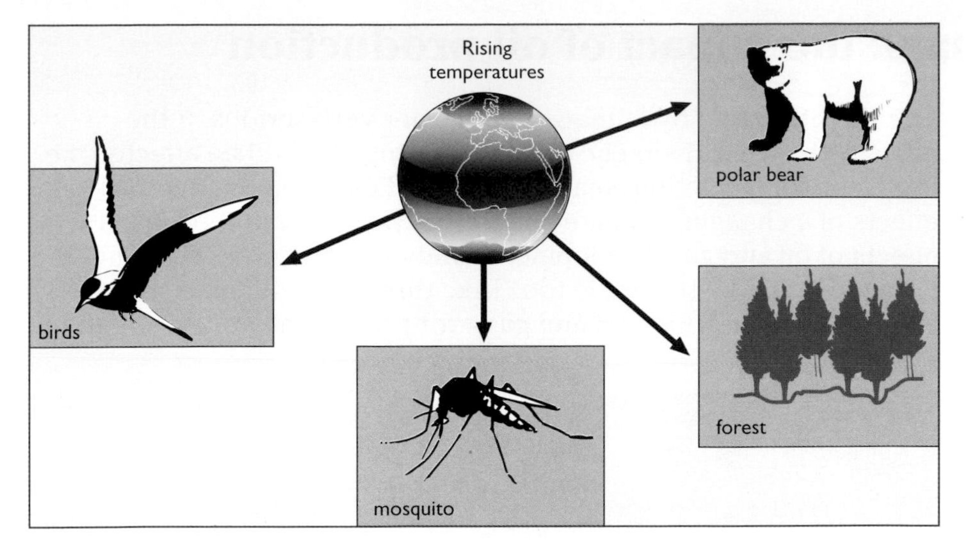

RESOURCE 3.12
Some of the impacts of global warming at the local scale.

Who is responsible?

Resource 3.13 is a table showing the percent of **carbon dioxide emissions** since 1800 by different areas of the world. The United States has 4% of the world's people, yet accounts for 25% of greenhouse gas emissions. At the 1997 meeting in Denver it was expected that the US would fall 13% short of the year 2000 target on greenhouse gases. The Worldwide Fund for Nature comparisons show that the North Americans are last in the industrialised countries in their efforts to curb climate change. Britain and Germany have two of the best records. Every government these days is meant to be both business friendly and also environmentally friendly. However it is difficult to achieve this. Multinational companies would lose out heavily if there were effective curbs on carbon emissions and deforestation. At the same time politicians will have to decide which is the higher priority, the environment or the business world.

If emissions continue to rise at the current rate, the global temperature will have increased by 1 to 3.5°C by 2100 and sea levels will have increased by 1 metre. The more developed nations will not be taken seriously by the developing nations until they can get their own house in order. There is also the need to make multinational corporations and the World Bank more environmentally conscious.

RESOURCE 3.13
CO_2 emissions.

Region	%
North America	35%
Western Europe	26%
Asia	13.3%
Former USSR	13.2%
Eastern Europe	6.6%
Latin America	2.9%
Oceania	1.2%

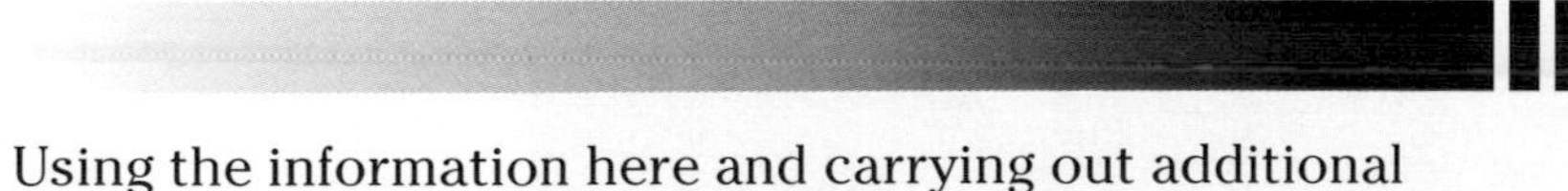

12. Using the information here and carrying out additional research design an information poster that informs people about climate change and the issues involved. You may want to ask different people their views and remember to use a variety of styles of presentation such as: maps, images, facts, bullet points, interviews.

The case of Yamal: the impact of oil production

The threats posed by **climatic change** are very serious. If the climate changes adversely, then everything else will be affected, i.e. crops, food production, sea levels around cities etc. The global effects of a changing climate certainly dwarf the more localised effects of oil and gas developments and disasters on the ground. But we should look at this scale too. Take three very different environments in which oil and gas – for they usually occur together – are exploited:

RESOURCE 3.14
One of the thousand burning oil wells in Kuwait, 1991.

1. *The North Sea, and British oil ports*: in the 1990s, two major oil spills occurred – the Braer tanker ran aground off the Shetlands in 1993, and the Sea Empress tanker on entering Milford Haven in S. Wales in 1996.
2. *The Kuwati Desert*: in the 1991 Gulf War – itself a product of conflict over energy resources – Saddam Hussein's flaring of the Kuwaiti desert oil wells brought news of a different scale of environmental disaster (Resource 3.14)
3. *The Russian Tundra*: Resource 3.15 illustrates how the development of oil and gas has affected the Russian tundra on many levels.

Russia is the world's biggest oil producer, and yet it is ranked 68th in world plastics production (a process that involves a great deal of oil).What this indicates is that Russia is a strong primary producer of raw materials – which are largely exported – and a weak manufacturer. Russian authorities are keen to develop oil and gas resources for industrial use.

The River Ob – at one time the producer of 60% of the former USSR's freshwater fish – now has fish stocks destroyed along 28 of its tributaries.

Surgut, a 300 000 population oil city, has a waste gas using plant, which pollutes the city.

Near Surgut, on the River Ob, a huge modern plastics factory has been approved.

The recent trend of encouraging capitalist western companies to bring in finance has resulted in companies – such as the petrochemical consortium NESTE, which has had factories closed in Sweden and Finland due to improper management of its waste product – opening vast factories in Russia.

The natural vegetation of the tundra – dwarf shrubs, coniferous forests, mosses and lichens – are fragile due to the nature of growth in a cold environment. To date over 250 000 square miles has been destroyed.

The Yamal peninsula, like much of the tundra, is largely uninhabited, but for thousands of years about 10 000 Nentsy people have survived there. Their traditional lifestyle is sustainable and does no harm to the environment.

RESOURCE 3.15
The Yamal Peninsula.

RESOURCE 3.16
The Taz-zivere region of the Russian tundra, in autumn.

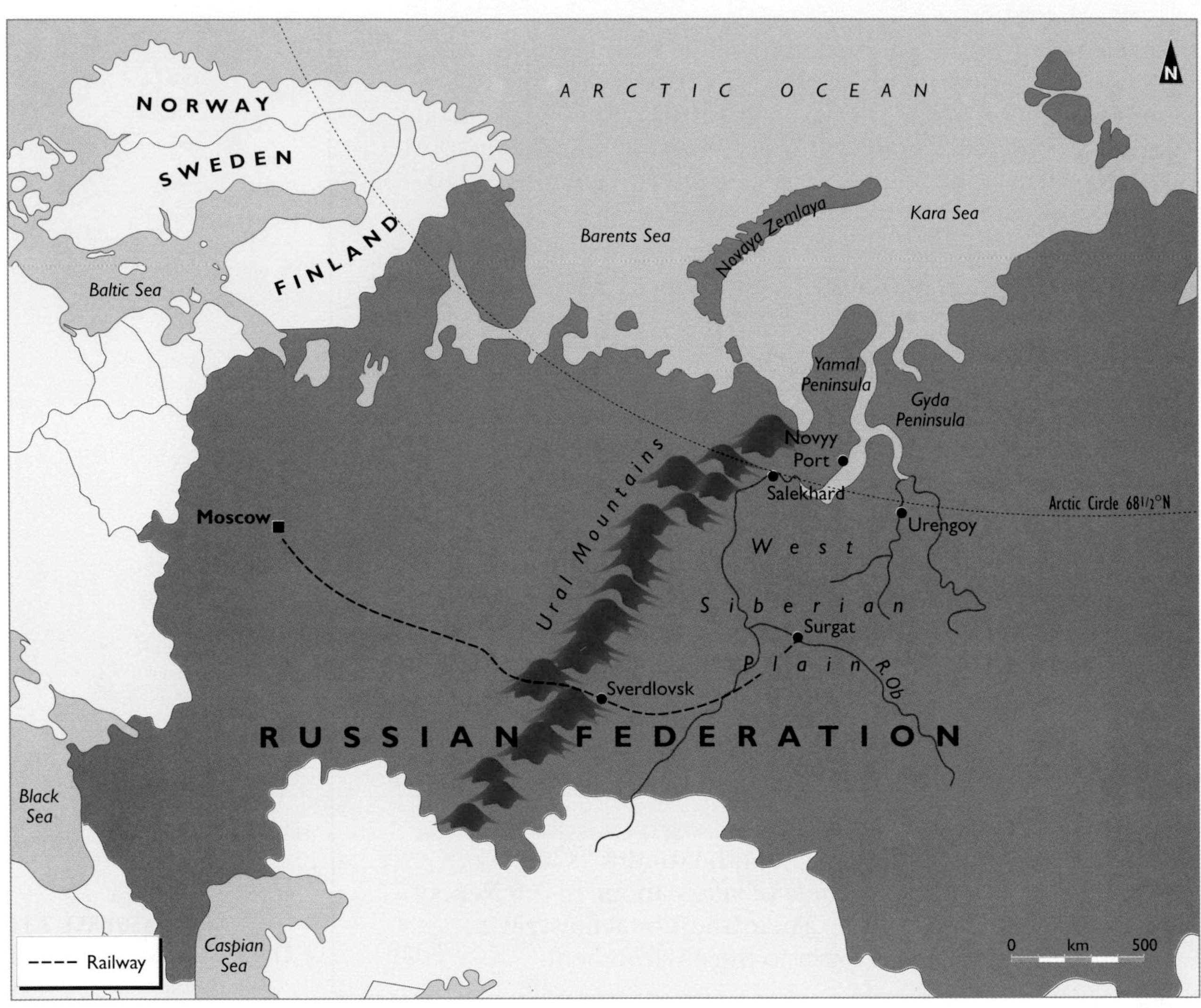

RESOURCE 3.17
Map of the Yamal and surrounding area.

13. Produce a sketch of the map of Yamal (Resource 3.17), and annotate it with the information provided in Resource 3.15. Then summarise that information in the form of a spider diagram, illustrating the linkages between topics such as:
    climate
    physical landscape
    energy development
    manufacturing
    international trade
    local population
    regional development
    political decision-making

Renewing the idea of renewables

WHAT IS RENEWABLE?

Renewable energy is power from a source that is able to replace itself. As potential users of that energy we have to use efficient methods to capture it. **Resource 3.17** shows pictures of three major types of renewable energy and **Resource 3.18** summarises those and other sources.

Renewable energy has been a source of energy from early times. Ever since humans have had the ability to organise ourselves into social groups we have always looked for ways to trap energy in order to allow us to function more efficiently and progress. The first source of power to be utilised was the sun. Aborigines, one of the earliest groups of people, relied on the sun to provide a source of energy in the form of fire. Throughout history we have continuously looked for new energy sources and more importantly new ways to trap that energy. In the days of early exploration wind power was used to propel boats across the seas. It was later trapped to turn windmills, now we are looking at wind power to provide us with an alternative for our traditional sources of energy, coal and oil. However the case of renewable energy is not without problems. It is seen as an expensive alternative and it is doubted that enough energy will be produced to sustain our current levels of demand and allow for continued expansion.

RESOURCE 3.18
Three main types of renewable energy, hydro power, wind power and solar power.

RESOURCE 3.19
Characteristics of different types of renewable energy.

Type	Brief description	Location	Methods used to capture it
Solar	Energy is trapped from the sun	Global, although the further away from the equator there is less intensity.	Solar panels Distillation of water e.g. salt production Solar thermo-electric plants Solar powered machines. Solar photovoltaics – direct production of energy from sunlight. Solar pond – developed in Israel Passive solar design – e.g. designing buildings retain or reflect heat.
Hydro	Energy is trapped from water	Fast flowing or falling water.	Watermills – traditional methods used. Turbines – a modern development used in HEP schemes.
Tidal	Energy is used from incoming and outgoing tides	Tidal areas – coastal	A small scale scheme based on the idea of a watermill. Limited potential due to small scale.
Wave	The movement of waves is used to produce energy.	Coastal areas	Wave-generators. Ideas are limited with minimal impact.
Geothermal	Energy is used from the earth's internal heat source – see Chapter 2	Areas affected by volcanic activity, e.g. Iceland, Japan	Direct use – e.g. 'balneology – spas and hot baths as well as industry and horticulture Drilling deep into the ground.
Wind	The force of the wind is trapped.	Exposed windy areas e.g. coastal areas, high moorland	Windmills are one of the earliest methods used. Since then this basic idea has been further developed from sail windmills to present day wind turbines.
Biomass	Use of vegetation to produce power	Anywhere there is an adequate supply of raw material	Oldest form is burning wood. Present day uses have extended this basic idea e.g. using woodchip or straw to produce energy for homes from a central plant.
Rubbish	Use of waste from a number of sources. the idea of recycling. Not a naturally occurring idea, but involves	Often located near to sources of rubbish, e.g. landfill sites and battery farms.	e.g. (i) Methane gas from landfill sites is used to provide gas. e.g. (ii) Chicken litter from battery farms can be turned into power.

14. Study **Resource 3.19** and write an account about renewable energy. Include information on the sources of renewable energy and some of the issues associated with its development.

15. Find out examples of renewable energy production based in your own area. Map your findings as in the example from East Anglia.

Resource 3.20 shows the sorts of renewable energy that are used in East Anglia. All these ideas are currently being researched to see if they can really work.

RESOURCE 3.20
Renewable energy in East Anglia.

Tidal: Research has been carried out into developing tidal power in The Wash. A barrage system would be used across the mouth of the estuary. There is potential but the shape of the estuary is not ideal and tidal range is small

Biomass: Trees can be grown amongst normal crops to provide the fuel source. The trees also act as effective windbreaks and can increase crop production. However the key factor in all of this is the lack of MONEY. It costs individual farmers too much to initiate these schemes

Wave: A turbine could be used to develop a wave generated power station. Wave power has limited potential if we use present day technology and the use of coastal areas to produce this energy can lead to habitat loss and environmental damage

Chicken litter: East Anglia produces more chicken litter than any other area in the UK. In the past the manure produced from these chicken and turkey units has been spread onto the fields, however this has led to concern about levels of nitrates in the soil. New legislation has meant that new ways have had to be found to dispose of this manure. It can be transformed into energy. It creates less damage than coal and oil and currently supplies 45 000 people with electricity

North Sea
The Wash
Barrage system
NORFOLK
Norwich
Fountain Renewable Resources
Diss
Fibrowatt
CAMBRIDGESHIRE
Cambridge Des Ltd
Cambridge
Wood Green
SUFFOLK
Ipswich
BEDFORDSHIRE
Shankley McEwan Group
Colchester
ESSEX
N
0 km 50

- County boundaries
- Main towns
- Case study locations

Rubbish: Even though recycling is important we still throw away 90% of our rubbish. Most ends up on landfill sites, where it is buried and then used to reshape the land. There is a build-up of methane gas. Wells can be dug into the rubbish and the methane can be converted to fuel. This has been done in Bedfordshire where it produces electricity for 9000 people

Wind: East Anglia is one of the windiest regions of Europe. It is flat and low lying. But it can cost a lot and some people object because the wind turbines do look as if they come from another planet. However for decades we have littered the landscape with electricity pylons. Which is worse?

Resource 3.21 shows how important water has been as a source of power over the centuries. The concept of water as a power source has not changed. What has changed is our ability to harness the potential it provides. For centuries watermills provided important energy but today we require more energy than they can provide.

RESOURCE 3.21
Timeline of hydro power.

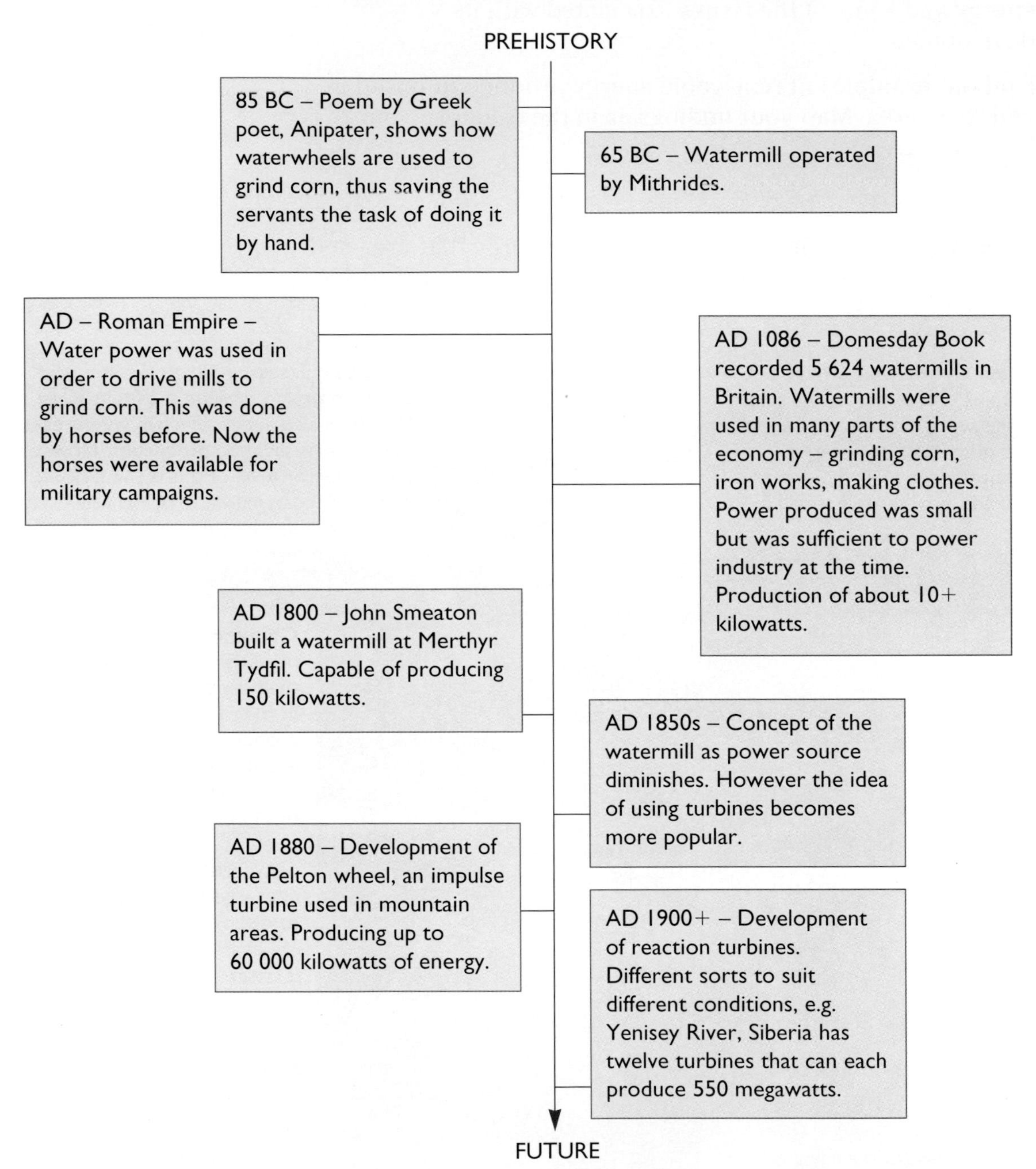

As with all sources of renewable energy there are many questions that need to be answered in order to ensure that we have an efficient and reliable source of power. The key question asked is 'What will be the **impact** of this scheme?' Research into the development of new environmentally friendly ways to capture these resources is constantly being made in order to gain the approval of the public. Study the following two schemes and try to assess if renewable energy has a place in our future energy strategy.

Case Study 1: Dinorwig pumped storage power station – Wales

> 'In a few thousand years time archaeologists may come across these workings and marvel how we did it with the machinery available at the time. Perhaps they will think this had some religious purpose'
>
> *Bill Thompson – site engineer at Dinorwig in 1983.*

The Dinorwig scheme came into operation in 1983. At the time it was the biggest underground power station in Europe. Nevertheless it is an example of a small scale Hydro Electric Power scheme.

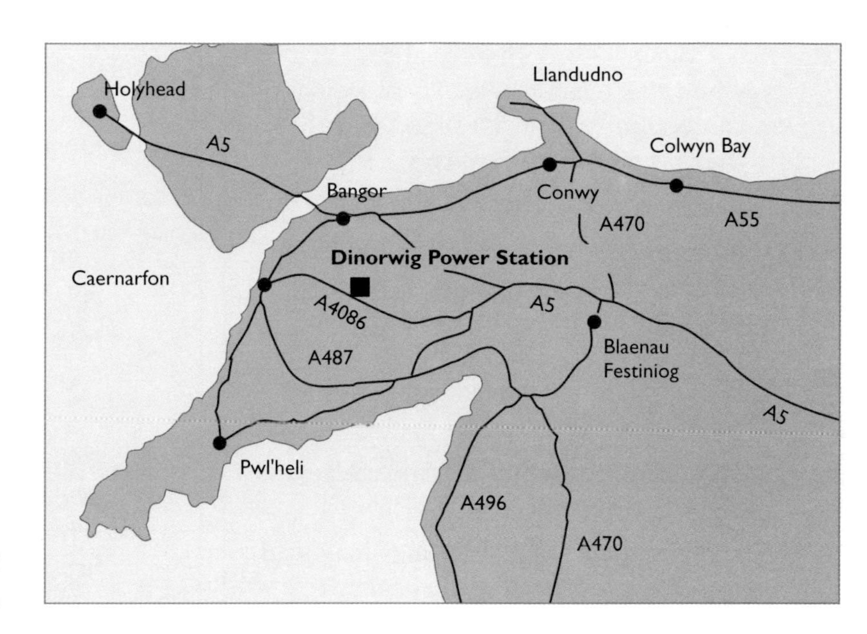

RESOURCE 3.22
Dinorwig.

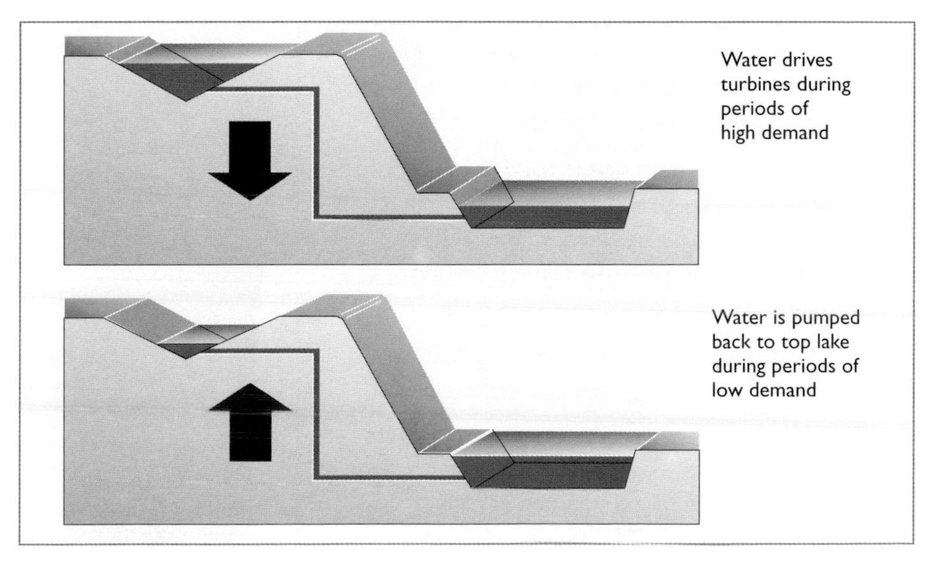

RESOURCE 3.23
Hydro-electric power.

KEY FEATURES OF THE DINORWIG SCHEME

- Small scale.
- Framework for the system was already in place with the existence of the former slate mine workings, therefore there was no need for flooding and disruption to the local area and people. Only modifications needed. Recycles a landuse.
- Responds quickly to local demand, e.g. during TV commercial breaks when there is a power surge demand can be met within 10 seconds as there is a storage facility.
- Water is recycled.
- Water is pumped from the lower lake, Llyn Peris back up to the top reservoir, Marchlyn Mawr, at night. Electricity is needed for this, therefore it is done at night when there is least demand.
- Minimal environmental damage as it is an underground site.
- Former slate mine workings may lead to some problems with respect to stability.
- Some environmental impact. A rare fish, the char, was found in Llyn Peris. It was left there when the last glaciers withdrew. Successful attempts were made to provide for this fish.
- Jobs were provided for local people during its construction. On completion these jobs went. Only need a few people for maintenance.
- No displacement of the local community, no valleys flooded, no major loss of good agricultural land.
- The scenery has been preserved as far as possible and Dinorwig is an area of outstanding natural beauty as **Resource 3.21** shows.

MAJOR FEATURES OF SMALL SCALE SCHEMES

- A lot of potential for energy production worldwide.
- Well suited to providing electricity for rural communities.
- No need for a large supply of water in the form of reservoirs, therefore eliminates problems associated with this issue.
- However no large storage facility does mean that demand may not be met at peak times.
- Environmentally friendly – small environmental impact.
- Dependent on local conditions, e.g. sufficient supply of water all year round.
- May lead to community involvement, especially in areas of rural decline.
- A local supply may help to attract small scale businesses.
- In developing countries small scale schemes may give local people their first supply of electricity.

RESOURCE 3.24 Dinorwig region.

Case Study 2: Three Gorges – China

Midway between its icy source in Tibet and the fertile delta at its mouth in Shanghai, 3 900 miles to the east, China's Yangtze river hurtles through a series of sheer chasms, known as the Three Gorges. Legend has it that the scenic channel was carved in stone by the goddess Yao Ji as a way of diverting the river around the petrified remains of a dozen dragons she had slain for harassing the peasants over the centuries. Such is the image and reverence that Chinese folklore has associated with the Three Gorges. Since the early part of the 20th century plans have been made to capture the power of this river and control the flood waters and provide power. It was first proposed in the 1920s. In 1953 Mao-Tse-tung returned to the plans when the Yangtze flooded and claimed 30 000 lives. However it was not until the 1990s that plans were turned to reality and work began on the dam.

RESOURCE 3.25
Map of China and 3 Gorges Dam.

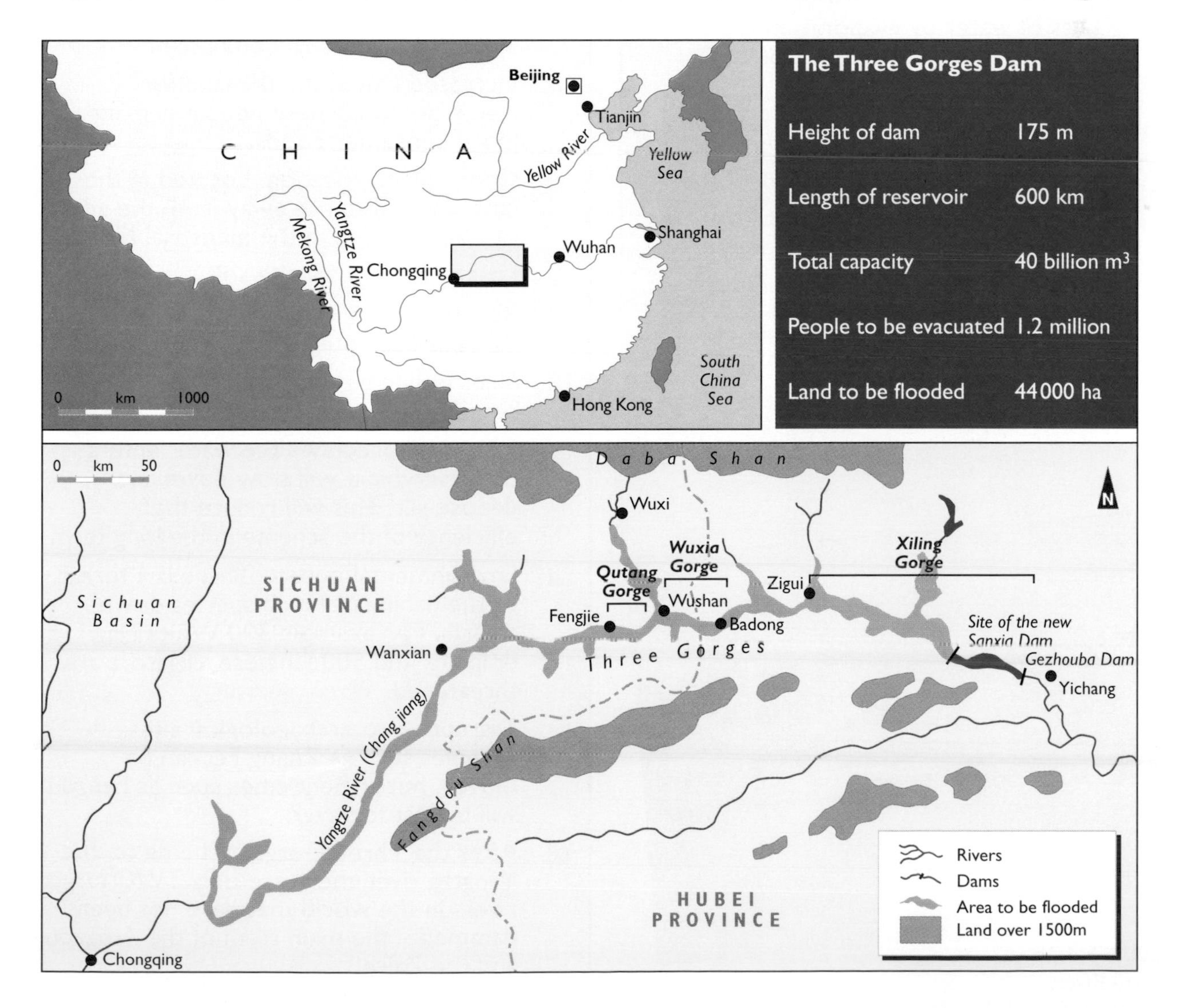

The Three Gorges Dam	
Height of dam	175 m
Length of reservoir	600 km
Total capacity	40 billion m^3
People to be evacuated	1.2 million
Land to be flooded	44000 ha

MAJOR FEATURES OF LARGE SCALE HYDRO SCHEMES

- Account for the majority of power produced by HEP schemes.
- Most dams are built for flood control as opposed to the production of HEP.
- Ability to generate large amounts of electricity.
- Favoured by ELDCs as opposed to EMDCs.
- Financing the development of schemes is important, often international help is needed.
- Flooding and construction of such schemes often leads to displacement of people.
- Loss of environmentally sensitive areas.
- Loss of water by evaporation is often large due to large amounts of water being exposed in a reservoir.
- Life expectancy of a scheme is limited due to silting. Water slows down near to the dam, therefore silt is deposited.
- Loss of fertility to soil in areas that would formerly have been flooded.
- Social impact, loss of communities and ways of life.

RESOURCE 3.26
Yangtse River.

KEY FEATURES OF THE THREE GORGES SCHEMES

- Vital statistics – Dam projected to be over 2 km in length. Reservoir will be 600 km. Generating capacity of 18 000 megawatts.
- Projected completion by 2009.
- Relocation of 1.2 million people. Loss of several cities, 140 towns, 4 500 villages.
- Estimated cost of 204 billion yuan (£16 billion).
- No international funding available due to opposition by other countries.
- Periodic flooding will be prevented. During 20th century over 500 000 people lost their lives due to floods.
- Reduce China's reliance on coal as a power source and all the problems associated with coal combustion.
- Increased rise in the demand for electricity as Chinese people demand more consumer goods.
- Geographical location. Located in the east, some distance away from the areas of main demand in the industrial North.
- Loss of fertility for the soil.
- Region is seismically active – earthquakes could damage the structure.
- Ships would be able to use the upper courses of the Yangtze.
- Silting will occur. As the water enters the reservoir it will slow down and deposit silt. This will reduce the efficiency of the scheme in the long term.
- Environmental impact. There is a threat to the habitats of rare species down stream. For example 300 White Flag dolphins and 500 Chinese alligators are threatened.
- Disruption to archaeological sites. Temples such as Zhang Fei can be moved, but ancient cities such as Fengdu will be lost for ever.
- After the Three Gorges scheme on the Yangtze river there are only TWO large rivers in the world that have not been dammed – the main stem of the Amazon and the Zaire!!

16. Using the information in these two case studies, outline the differences between the small scale and the large scale. State the positive and negative impacts of each scheme. You might want to carry out an Environmental Assessment in the way you did in Chapter one.
17. Do you think hydro electric power has a role in our future energy strategy? If it does then at what cost and what form should it take?

A question of energy?

How should we set about developing a sustainable energy strategy? Throughout this chapter you have had the opportunity to learn about different forms of energy and the issues associated with the provision of a reliable energy supply. Imagine what it would be like to wake up to no power. There would be plenty of it around but it would not be in the form that you could use.

18. Make a copy of the following table and complete it with details of the type of energy you use at the start of the day

Time	Activity	Equipment Used	Energy Source Used
0700	Wake Up	Stereo	Electricity, from national grid

Your list will show you just how dependent we are on someone giving us the power to be able to manoeuvre ourselves around this planet on a daily basis.

What is meant by a 'secure and reliable' energy supply?

Governments and electricity companies are usually charged with being responsible for the development of a 'secure and reliable' supply of energy for the nation/region/customers. What exactly does this mean? It seems that there are several contexts in which a power supply can be regarded as 'secure and reliable'. These are so important that a study of energy at any level should take them into account. We identify here four ways in which they can apply:

1. THE ENERGY SUPPLY SHOULD BE 'FAILSAFE'

In any country or region, the demand for energy varies considerably over time. Clearly, if the supply of electricity falls short of this fluctuating demand, even for a moment, then the whole system is liable to 'crash', as not infrequently happens in some developing countries.

2. THE ENERGY SUPPLY SHOULD PRESENT A *BALANCED* 'MIX', (DIVERSITY)

The oil crisis of the mid-1970s, in which world oil prices quadrupled virtually overnight, showed the great importance of not becoming over-dependent on a single, or too few, sources of energy. The opposite of 'over-dependence' is 'diversity', which is summed up by the phrase 'Don't put all your eggs in one basket'. The dangers of specialising in too few sources are real and serious. So, as a nation's economy matures, it is also likely to diversify its energy supply systems, meaning that its energy 'portfolio' of mix will be more complex and the sources of energy be more numerous, balanced and varied. This gives the government more stability, and more options in times of future economic, or even military stress.

3. THE ENERGY SUPPLY MUST BE *LITERALLY* SECURE

The supplies of energy within a country must also be secure from terrorism or from potential future military opponents.

4. WHAT ABOUT THE SECURITY OF THE ENVIRONMENT?

In other words, how sustainable is the supply of energy? This can be in terms of how long can the use of the current mix last, at the current rates of consumption? Secondly, what is the current mix doing to the environment? Finally, what is being done to deal with that environmental damage?

In order to develop an effective energy strategy we need not only to think about where it comes from and how it can be used, but also that there is enough diversity so that it is sustainable in human and environmental terms.

HUMANS AS BALANCERS

4

Key Idea

A key area of international concern is finding ways in which we can work to a sustainable future. This is a real life issue for which there is no single easy answer. It is important to see how decisions are made about the environment and know what really is sustainable. How long will it take to become sustainable and how far is it desirable?

RESOURCE 4.1
Humans as balancers.

What do the professionals think?

You will have your own ideas about the environment and how we should approach managing it, so do lots of other people. **Resource 4.2** shows two different attitudes to the environment.

RESOURCE 4.2
Extreme attitudes

	Extreme economist	Extreme environmentalist
VALUES	Economic development and the raising of people's material living standards must always have priority.	Economic development is only acceptable if it has no adverse effects on the environment.
BELIEFS	Wealth has to be generated in the first place if people are to enjoy the environment.	Industrial development causes irreversible damage to the environment, including loss of species, wildlife and habitat.
	The environment is a distraction which would raise costs, limiting a country's ability to compete internationally.	The quality of life is not measurable just in terms of income and material possessions.
	Damage to the environment is localised and its overall impact is exaggerated.	We have no right to destroy the environment. We have a duty to protect it for future generations.
	As people's material needs are met it will be possible to give conservation a higher priority.	Industrial development benefits governments and large industrial corporations rather than the people. It is ordinary people who suffer the consequences of environmental destruction and pollution.
ATTITUDE	In favour of industrialisation.	Against industrialisation.

1. Draw two large images of human beings, one for each of the following:

   Extreme economist; extreme environmentalist.

2. For each, give the character a suitable name and annotate the image with information from **Resource 4.3**. Use suitable images to help illustrate what each one is like.
3. Draw a third image. Label this 'accommodator'. Fill in the characteristics you think this person would have. We will be exploring this attitude further.

No more mountains to climb!

We looked at systems in Chapter 1. Now we will see how systems can be messed up and what the consequences are.

A Case Study of Grasberg Mountain, West Papua

Grasberg Mountain is the site of a mining development in a very remote part of the world, on the western side of the large tropical island of New Guinea. **Resource 4.4** is a map showing its location. Here, an American multinational corporation (MNC) called Freeport has developed one of the world's biggest open pit copper and gold mines.

RESOURCE 4.3 Grasberg Mountain, West Papua.

RESOURCE 4.4
Map of Grasberg Mountain, West Papua.

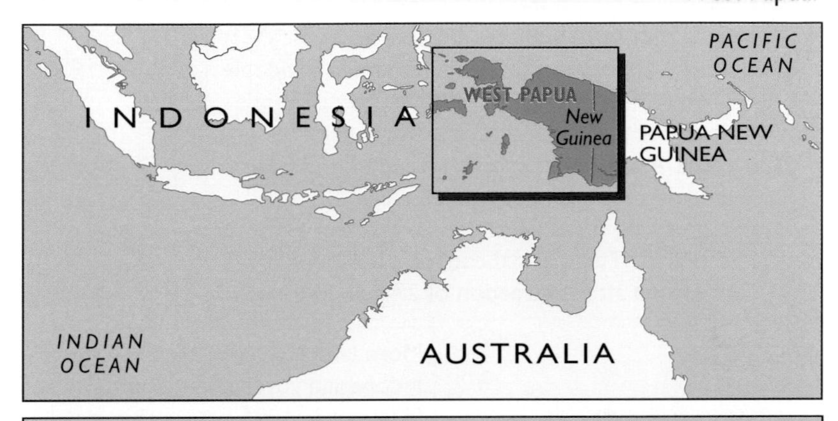

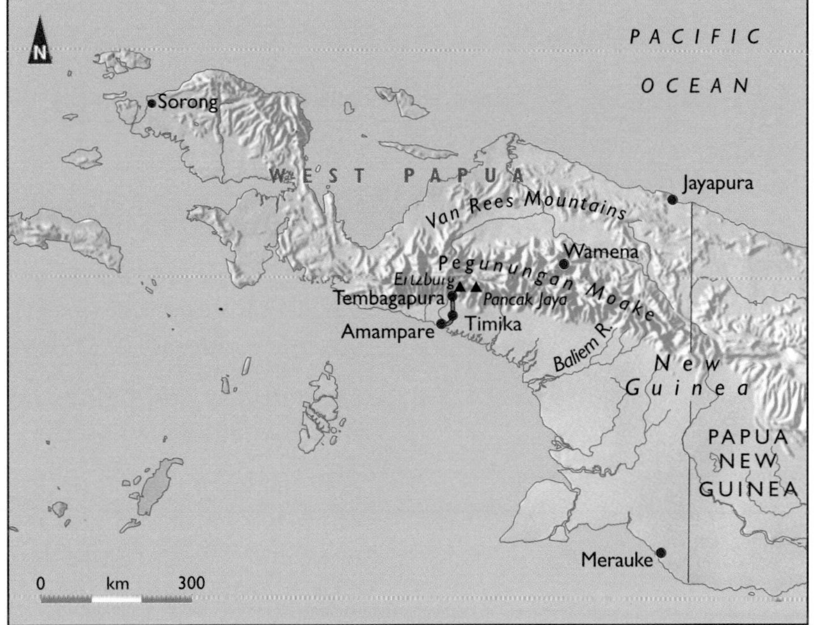

4. Study carefully the information contained in **Resource 4.5 and 4.6**. Using only economic costs weigh up whether you think the mine should have gone ahead as it did. Give reasons. Now examine the whole set of factors and answer the same question. Should the mine have gone ahead? Give reasons for your opinion.

14 million years ago, major plate collision produces metal ores in the mountain spine of New Guinea.

1960 – Having remained a curiosity for many years, the Freeport Sulphur Company are the first to lead expeditions to Puncak Joya.

1936 – A Dutch geologist climbs Puncak Joya and discovers outcrop of copper.

1967 – In agreement with the Indonesian government, the *Freeport Indonesia* company established.

1963 – Annexation of West Papau, a Dutch colony, by Indonesia, without the consent of its people.

Trouble between Indonesian government and residents unhappy about annexation worsens: West Papuan villages are bombed and hundreds of people are killed in the fighting. The OPM (Operasi Paptia Merdeka) form, intending to provide resistance to Indonesia. Armed with spears, machetes and bows and arrows, they are initially ineffective.

1970 – Feasibility study of the area concluded, copper extraction begins culminating in the first shipment (to Japan) in 1972.

1988 – Gold is discovered on the neighbouring Grasberg mountain. Mining begins in 1990, culminating in 25 000 tonnes being mined per day by 1992.

1989 – The original copper mining operation closed after extraction of 27 million tonnes.

More land conceded to the company by the Indonesian government. Renewed resistance followed. In 1995 troops shot dead 11 civilians. In 1996, the Jakarta regime initiate an enquiry into the problems, with an eye on finally reaching some kind of peace.

RESOURCE 4.5
Timeline of Grasberg.

5. What sort of factors do you think the Freeport company and the Indonesian Government took into consideration when they decided to develop the mine.
6. Explain why companies do not always take into account ALL the factors when they develop such resources.
7. Is it easier to calculate the economic costs or the social, environmental and cultural costs? Give reasons for your answers. What are the dangers of not giving full consideration to all types of costs?
8. There is a saying ‘Money talks’, but do you think such narrow bases for decision making are desirable? Give reasons for your opinions.
9. How well do you think the Freeport and the Indonesian Government have performed in their task of being ‘Stewards’ of the West Papuan environment? Give reasons for your answer.
10. How sustainable is the Grasberg mine development? Give evidence for your answer.

COSTS

Economic	difficult mine location: 70 miles into the interior, in dense rainforest and alpine peaks
	need to build a sea-port at Amamapare, plus inland airstrip at Timika, plus building the (only) 63 mile road to the site
	construction of a mill site, as the ore is suitable for primary treatment locally
	immense support services are needed for minerals extraction and processing: $3 billion was invested
Social	the Amungme people have lost their ancestral mountain homes to the mines and have been forced to resettle on the coast with only the barest compensation
	a further 2 000 people are threatened with eviction to make way for the mine's expansion
	there have been regular rebel attacks on the mine, as the biggest source of friction in the territory
	atrocities have been perpetrated, tortures and killings, as rebels are suppressed
	American miners' wives live a confined life
Environmental	for scientists and explorers, the heart of New Guinea ranks along with the Amazon Basin as one of the planet's last two great wildernesses
	the new 2.6 million ha. land concession in 1994, 250 times bigger than the existing one threatens a much wider area of mountain rainforest
	the mine has caused pollution
	waste dumped into the nearest valley
	the mine, when it is all over, will inevitably leave one of the greatest messes on the face of the earth. Nothing can be done to cover it up.
Cultural	the mine has excavated a sacred mountain, and there are claims that traditional tribal land-rights have been ignored
	the Amungme people were/are hunter-gatherers, and have been/are resettled in Tembagapura, and have lost 10 000 ha., for which nothing has been paid
	these minority people have developed their own culture, are now being persuaded or compelled to surrender to the central government, the resources upon which they and their ancestors have lived
	a large and powerful Protestant mission is actively working to convert the Amungme

BENEFITS

Economic	here exists one of the 3 largest open pit gold reserves in the world and one of the 5 largest open pit copper reserves in the world, mined in conjunction: it is one of the most profitable mines on earth
	the ore is of extraordinary rich concentration: 1.3% copper, plus 1.4 grammes of gold and 4.1 grammes of silver per tonne
	in 1994 Grasberg produced 75 000 tonnes of ore per day, in a ratio of 2 copper to 1 gold
	such developments have given Indonesia a voice at the tables of some of the world's most exclusive clubs
	Indonesia's biggest earner of foreign exchange
	provides 10 000 men with jobs, of which 700 are American, and the rest virtually all immigrant Indonesian
	the achievement of almost unbelievable feats of engineering
Social	the company mining settlement at Tembagapura, (pop. 100 000 and growing) has a superbly equipped hospital
	schools have been built by Freeport for the Amungme
Environmental	???
Cultural	???

RESOURCE 4.6
Grasberg Mountain: A cost-benefit analysis.

The scale of decision making

Making a decision about something is a complex process. There are many different levels to decision making. The following activity will demonstrate the complexity of decision making for a small area of Spain. You make decisions every day of your life. It may be a simple one about what you are going to wear. Or it may be a complex one like where to go on holiday with your family. In the latter case it will affect several people. Each person will have their own ideas about what they want from the holiday. The same principles can be applied to decisions that are made about planning issues. There are many people and many levels that have to be consulted in order to ensure the correct plan is used. **Resource 4.7** shows the many different issues involved in the decision to locate a housing development. In the following activity you will be involved in the complex procedure of actively seeking and giving of permission for a number of projects that are part of 'The Ronda Plan'.

RESOURCE 4.7
Decisions to locate housing development.

SCALE	a. ECONOMIC	b. SOCIAL	c. DEMOGRAPHIC	d. POLITICAL	e. TECHNICAL	f. PHYSICAL
1. NATIONAL	The general state of the economy.	Changes in tenure.	Population growth rates. Migration. Changes in population structure.	Housing legislation. Planning legislation.	Transport innovation affecting private sector (e.g. increase in car ownership). Innovation in construction industry (e.g. tower crane, reinforced concrete)	
2. REGIONAL	Employment structure. Ability of region to attract new jobs. Rates of unemployment.	Demographic and social characteristics of the region.		Regional planning policies		
3. LOCAL	Availability of land for development. The way in which adjoining land is used.	The perceived characteristics of the neighbourhood.	The age-sex structure of the residents of neighbouring housing districts.	Planning constraints. Local government policy.		Nature of the individual sites e.g. elevation, aspect, drainage. Accessibility of the site to the public. Transport and main road networks.

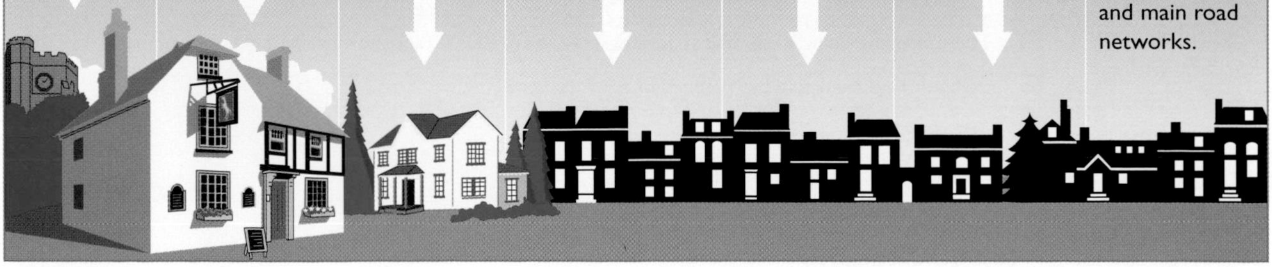

The setting

'BANDIDO COUNTRY'

The town of Ronda is located in the South west of the Spanish region of Andalucia. It is about 60 km west of the coastal resort of Torremolinos. It is set in the Sierra de Ronda, where mountains rise to about 3 600 ft above sea level. Ronda as a settlement is typical of this area, it is one of the 'White Towns', which are modest in their appearance but have a dramatic setting. Ronda is built on an isolated ridge. Sheer cliffs rise up on three sides and the old town is separated from the new town by 'El Tajo Gorge', through which the Rio Guadalevin flows.

The area is a stark contrast to the coastal area – Costa del Sol. It is famous for the bandits that used to terrorise travellers. Agriculture is an important economic activity. The area has 20 million square metres of native woodland. There is small scale tourist development, but so far this has had little impact on the area.

THE RONDA PLAN

In the early 1990s the Ronda Plan was proposed. It was aimed at large scale development of the area. The 20 000 000 m^2 of indigenous woodland and agricultural land was earmarked for large scale development of 6 golf courses and 2 500 houses. This is where you take the plan on board.

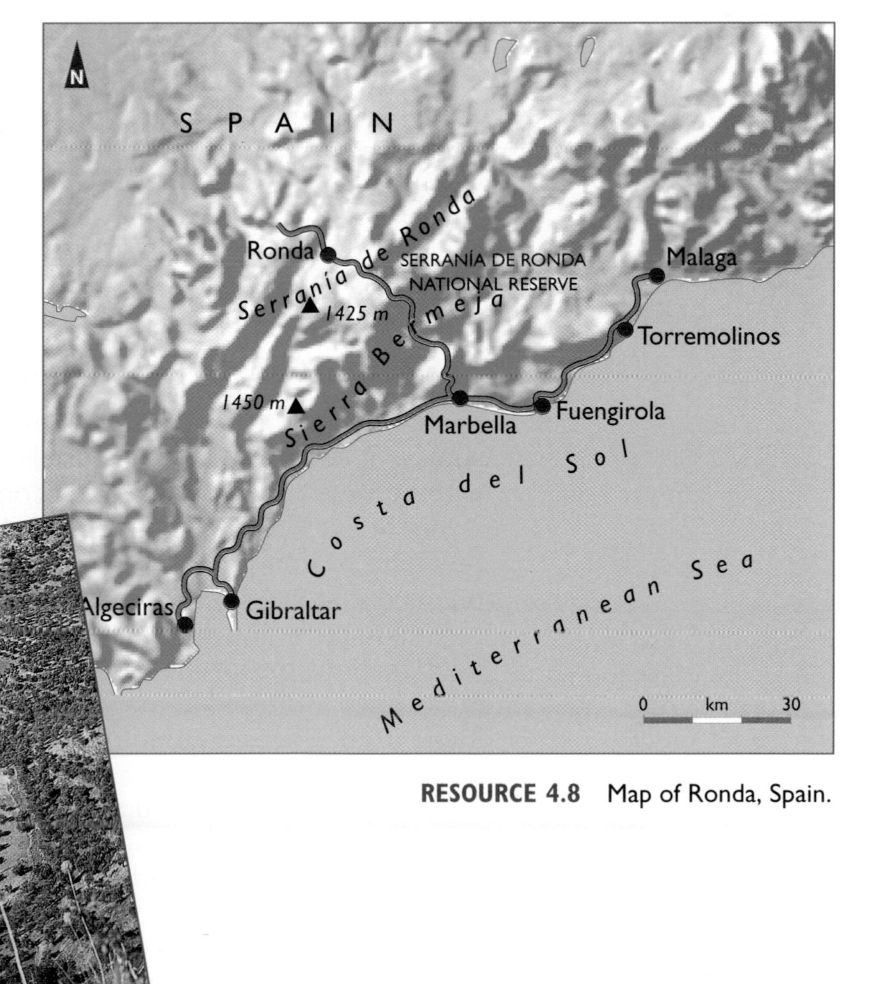

RESOURCE 4.8 Map of Ronda, Spain.

RESOURCE 4.9 Ronda, Spain.

11. Describe the effects the Ronda plan will have on the following:
    - small scale tourist developer
    - large scale tourist developer
    - small scale farmer
    - flamenco dancer
    - environmentalist
12. If you were a grant provider in the European Parliament responsible for agriculture what do you think your main concerns would be? Do the same for each of the following areas of responsibility: Tourism, Environment, Regional Development, National Development.
13. Imagine the development is going ahead. Think of the overall costs and benefits. Suggest ways in which it could be planned to balance these costs and benefits effectively.
14. Now, bearing all these issues in mind, write a report to say whether you would give funding or not and explain your reasons.

Growth and renewal

WHAT ARE THE ALTERNATIVES?

Resources can be managed to satisfy many demands. Maintaining a source of energy and raw materials can be balanced successfully with conservation, tourism and economic growth. In Britain we have a very active Forestry Commission. It was started in 1919 in response to a shortage of wood after the first world war. It was planned that in the event of a national crisis we would not have to rely on imported wood. Since then the Forestry Commission has been responsible for the planting of many areas of Britain with trees. It has been criticised in the past for the management strategies that it has used. However, today a definite effort has been made to diversify the function of the Forestry Commission. It is responsible for not only growing wood and providing us with the associated products but for promoting recreational activities, conservation projects, wildlife observation and heritage schemes.

Working towards a future?

Sustainable development is based upon two assets available to us.

1. **Natural assets:** the range of natural systems and resources, of which man is part. Some of these, such as the ozone layer, or tropical forests, are critical to the well-being of human kind. Once destroyed it may be impossible to recreate them. Other natural assets can be used more intensively (e.g. for minerals, arable crops or fisheries), or converted to human-made assets, without threat to our life support system or an unacceptable lowering of the quality of life.

2. **Human-made assets:** these assets that we have created to maintain the basic quality of our existence, e.g. houses, schools, hospitals, industrial plants, roads and technology, as well as human ingenuity.

The two most important approaches to environmental management suggested by sustainable development analysis are valuing the environment and placing an appropriate emphasis on longer-term factors.

Environmental economists say there are three things to consider when looking at total value of any environmental asset: the value of an environmental resource to all those who use it directly (forests, used now for fuel and the value of the resource to those who expect to use it in the future (green spaces, tourism) for future children to play in; the value of the resource to people who may never expect to use it, but derive satisfaction from knowing it exists (the Antarctic or the great whales). In this way sustainable development implies responsibility towards future generations.

Throughout the book we have seen that sustainable development involves the consideration of ecological, economic, cultural and social elements. These can be summarised:

Ecological sustainability: the maintenance of life support systems, biological diversity, and the achievement and maintenance of necessary standards of air and water quality.

Economic sustainability: making the best long-term use of our natural and human-made assets to maintain and where practicable, improve peoples' living standards.

Cultural sustainability: the conservation of our scenic quality, historical features and all that goes to create a unique sense of place.

Social sustainability: the maintenance of viable opportunities for communities of people to live and work.

Combine these issues and you should be able to develop a successful strategy for sustainability. These may seem large scale issues but they can be managed at the local scale.

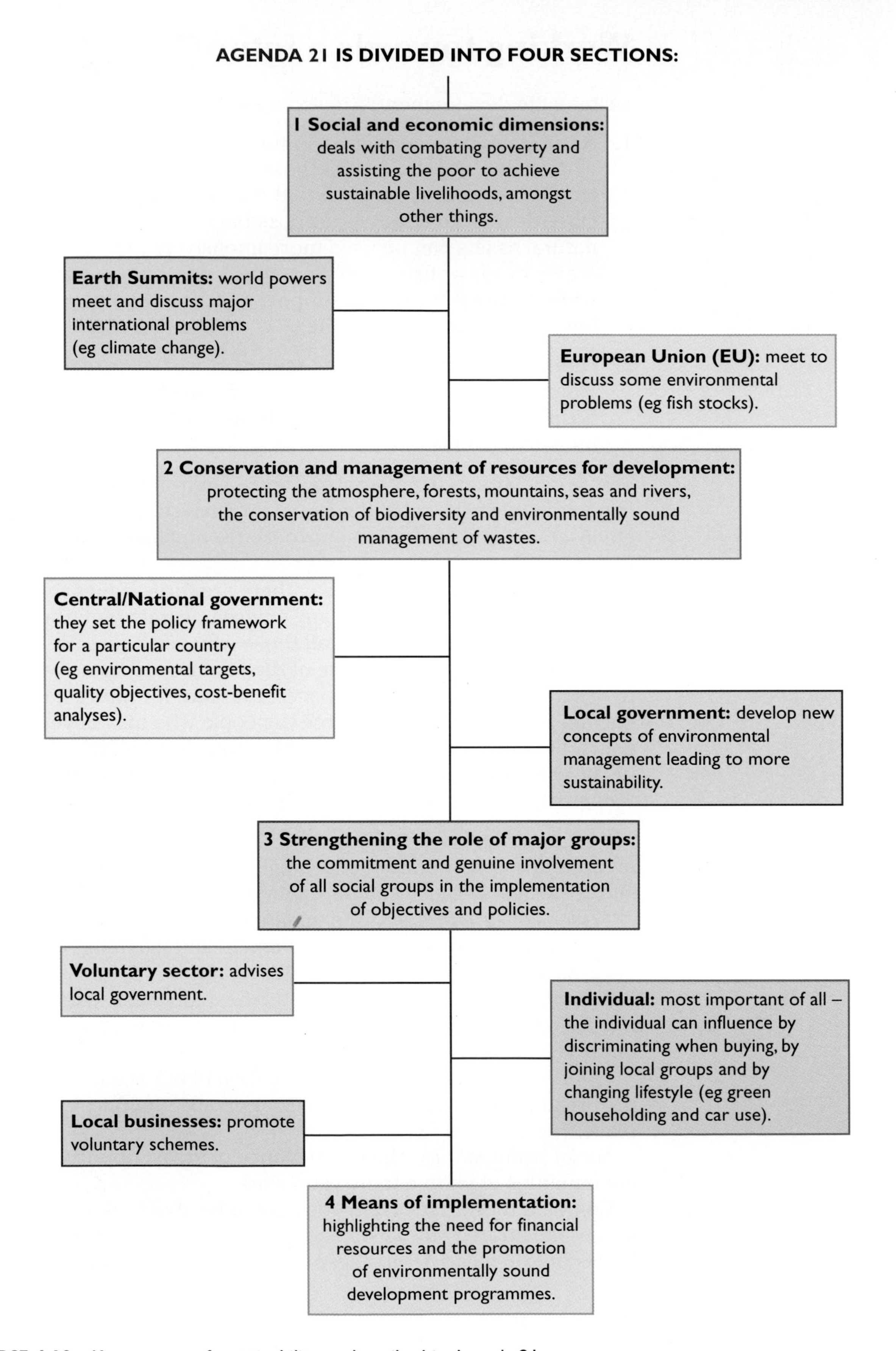

RESOURCE 4.10 Key aspects of sustainability as described in Agenda 21.

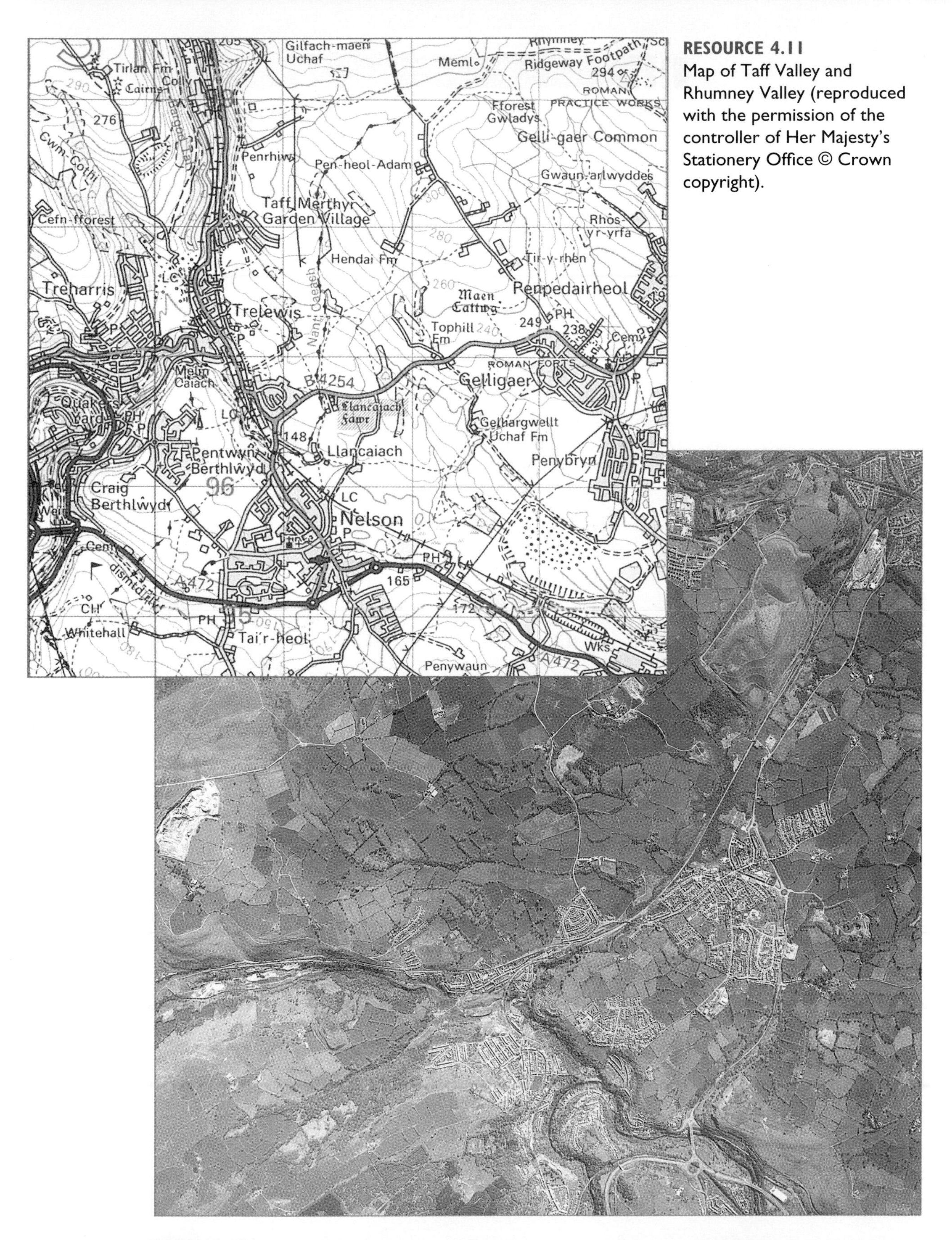

RESOURCE 4.11
Map of Taff Valley and Rhumney Valley (reproduced with the permission of the controller of Her Majesty's Stationery Office © Crown copyright).

RESOURCE 4.12
Aerial photo of Taff Valley and Rhumney Valley.

Putting Agenda 21 to work in the landscape

Study Resource 4.10, which provides you with some background to Agenda 21.

15. Resource 4.11 is the vertical aerial photograph of part of the landscape of South Wales, between the Taff Vale and the Rhymney Valley, about 20 km north of Cardiff. Compare the aerial photo with Resource 4.12, the 1:50 000 O.S. map extract of the same area. Discuss how and exactly where in this landscape you would develop schemes to fulfil the Agenda 21 obligation. Think about the ideas raised at the beginning of this section.

16. When you have an idea what needs doing, and where this landscape would offer you potential to go ahead and develop such schemes, take a large sheet of tracing paper, overlaid on the air photo, and

a) mark on some of the main physical and human features of this area, such as the valleys of the rivers Taff and Rhymney, major roads and settlements. Label these.

b) mark on the locations of schemes you have developed for the area.

c) label these and provide some description (either as annotation on the traced map itself or via a numbered 'tagging' system, with full explanation elsewhere) of how these schemes will hope to achieve Agenda 21 'goals', and why they are best located where you have placed them.

d) What problems and difficulties do you feel the schemes may run up against, especially in such a landscape as this.

A concluding thought!

You now should have an understanding of some of the issues associated with the idea of sustainability. It is a very complex topic and one which stimulates a lot of debate and discussion. In order to move forward humans face a number of options. There is no one single answer, just as there is no one single point of view. You have just entered into one of the biggest debates of our time. Good luck in your journey of finding out more and remember 'A task is like a postage stamp, its purpose is never fulfilled until it gets to the end', 'One who never makes mistakes, never makes anything'!

Enjoy the rest of your voyage of discovery.